No Turning Back

The inspiring story of the first Brethren in Christ missionaries

No Turning Back

The inspiring story of the first Brethren in Christ missionaries

By Carolyn Kimmel

Published by
Brethren in Christ World Missions

Printed by
Evangel Press

No Turning Back
ISBN-10: 1-933858-26-5
ISBN-13: 978-1-933858-26-5

Published by Brethren in Christ World Missions
© 2007 Brethren in Christ World Missions

To order additional copies please contact:
       Brethren in Christ World Missions
       Box 390, Grantham, PA 17027
       bicwm@messiah.edu
       www.bic-church.org/wm

Published 2007 by Brethren in Christ World Missions
All rights reserved. Except in the case of brief quotations in
critical articles or reviews, no part of this book may be
reproduced in any form without prior written permission from
Brethren in Christ World Missions,

Author: Carolyn Kimmel
Editorial team: John Brubaker, Nathan Stonge
Cover design: Katie Geshay
Interior design: Mark Burford, Evangel Press
Photographs: Courtesy Brethren in Christ Archives

Printed in the United States of America
by Evangel Press, Nappanee, IN

Researching the lives of early Brethren in Christ missionaries has been something of a treasure hunt, looking in many places and sometimes finding a nugget of something usable and other times, not. Along with me on the hunt was Brethren in Christ Archivist Gloria Stonge. I want to thank Gloria for her willing spirit, helpful wisdom and, most of all, her welcoming and encouraging smile every time I visited the archives.

—Carolyn Kimmel

Brethren in Christ World Missions sustains and facilitates a global ministry focus for the Brethren in Christ Church of North America by partnering with sister conferences and like minded-organizations across the world, enabling the emergence of multiplying communities of believers especially among the least reached peoples of the world. For more on the vision, mission and the entire BICWM team see the website listed on the facing page.

This booklet is the first of an anticipated three-part series that will also include a summary of the vision, mission and strategic priorities represented through the current breadth and scope of Brethren in Christ ministry worldwide.

Late May of 2005 I found myself staring at a blank computer screen in my office silently praying that God would give me his thoughts for the final elements of my upcoming Board for World Missions presentation. The pieces didn't quite seem to be in place yet. With a burst of inspiration I did a quick internet search for one of the earliest names I could remember in the history of Brethren in Christ Missions. I had heard only tangentially of David Zook's name and knew very little about him.

After a bit of fruitless effort, an unlinked page materialized in front of me that I have never been able to locate again through an internet search. It told the story of David and his siblings – a story completely new to me – through the song sheets printed at the conclusion of this book. In 1909, Herbert Buffum, one of the world's most prolific songwriters, composed a song based on the Zook family. As I eagerly pored over these online documents I realized that a very significant part of our history had somehow slipped into obscurity. The more I read, the more I knew that this story needed to be researched and retold to an emerging generation that embodies many of the same traits marking the generation that first helped launch global ministry among the Brethren in Christ.

I'm grateful to Carolyn Kimmel for spear-heading this research and recording the details of this story in a fresh format.

I continue to be deeply moved by the younger leaders around us who exhibit the same desire to live life on the edge—fully committed to usher in the Kingdom of God through lives completely abandoned to Christ.

John Allen Brubaker, 2007

TABLE OF CONTENTS

Prologue xi

The Zook Family xv

Chapter One: Inklings 1

Chapter Two: The Call Comes...........................17

Chapter Three: First Steps 27

Chapter Four: The Ultimate Cost.......................35

Chapter Five: The Next Wave 55

Chapter Six: From Their Genes to Ours?...........63

Epilogue..69

Living the Brethren in Christ Mandate 73

Sources..83

Timeline..87

The Missionaries' Home-Going 89

A Missionary's Letter To Her Parents 93

A MISSIONARY'S LETTER
To Her Parents.

Sripat Purunia, Bankura Dist., Bengal, India.
Dec. 31, 1907.

My Dear Papa and Mamma:—

"Bless the Lord, Oh my soul! and all that is within me, Bless His holy name!" Perhaps you wonder at my starting out thus. It is only because God gives me such victory at this time when the waters are deep and the furnace is hot. I suppose that sometime to-day you will receive the word of dear Josiah's home going. Yes, our precious Josiah, your dear boy and my darling husband. Oh can it be? It is the same old story. He came in contact with the smallpox somewhere. It has been at Raghunathpur and it goes through the air you know. He hadn't felt well for a couple of weeks and yet we still took a trip up country, he going, on to Lucknow and having a visit with Brother Mussers'. He felt it so on his heart to visit them. He felt the Lord was leading him to go and they had such a nice time together and explained some things and they seemed to understand some things in a way they hadn't before. He felt blessed in having gone. I will tell you more later. I met him at Mugalsari and then we went to Benares together, were at Arrah Sunday and on Monday we came here. He went to bed as soon as we got here and felt very sick that night. Each succeeding day

In the margins appear Mary Zook's handwritten comments on this early publication of her daughter Rhoda's last letter. The entire letter can be found beginning on page 93.

PROLOGUE

Mary Zook clutched the letter to her chest and hurried back into the small house she and her husband Noah called home, here in the Kansas countryside. The wind was bitter cold on this January day in the year 1908, but it was her heart that felt oddly cold at the moment. Mary didn't recognize the handwriting on this letter, yet it came from India, where her widowed daughter Rhoda was still grieving the loss of her husband Josiah to smallpox just two weeks earlier.

Mary smiled faintly at the memory of her last visit with Rhoda, and Josiah Martin, the man who had swept her missions-minded daughter off her feet and set her thoughts to things such as marriage and babies even as he shared her passion for taking the Gospel to those who had never heard it before.

The pictures of her precious grandchildren, Esther and Everett, just eleven months old, flashed in her mind as she opened the letter. Poor babies; they would never know their father, never know the feel of his large hand in theirs and never hear his testimony of love of the Lord.

"Oh no, dear God, no," Mary whispered as her eyes scanned the contents of the foreign letter. Tears involuntarily sprang to her eyes and a slow wail filled the room. It was her voice, but she was numb to it and powerless to stop it. Noah Zook ran in from the parlor at the sound of his wife's moans.

"Mary, my darling, what is it?" he cried out, rushing to her side. Mary couldn't speak, but thrust the letter toward him. He too scanned the first paragraph and felt the familiar horror creep into his soul and threaten to overtake his entire being.

"Again, Lord? Again? Must we bear this pain again?" he questioned aloud.

THE ZOOK FAMILY

Noah Zook – b. 1841 Chambersburg, PA
Mary Zook – b. 1846, Jacksonville, PA
m. 1860

David Zook
b. 1872, Franklin County, PA
m. 1893, Katie

Sara Zook (Cress)
b. 1874, Franklin County, PA
m. 1896 Clifford Cress

Eber Zook
b. 1875, Franklin County, PA
m. 1898, Amanda

Rhoda Zook (Martin)
b. 1881, Dickinson County, KS
m. 1900, Josiah Martin

(Three of Mary and Noah's children died in early
childhood; four others are not significantly referenced
in this work.)

Chapter One
Inklings

Fifteen Years Earlier

David Zook could not deny what he knew was taking place in his soul. A calling that had taken root and become a yearning–a yearning to tell people about Christ, and not just to tell them himself, but to urge others to do the same. And he knew he could not do this from a farm in Kansas.

"I see the example of my father and my mother, who find nothing more important than spreading the news of Christ," the third oldest son of Noah and Mary Zook told a young friend one evening as they made their way in from the farm fields. David drove a large hay wagon pulled by a pair of his father's strongest mules. "I think, Robert, that I feel that is true in my life as well."

He searched his boyhood friend's face for a reaction but saw only a look of confusion. His friend, it seemed, was happy enough to become a Kansas farmer who went to church on Sundays and lived his life out right here, like generations before him.

"Robert, when the Lord calls us, He has a field in which we are to work," David continued. "The call has come to me, that I should write to a brother and offer my services at the Faith Home at Tabor, Iowa, which I did. An answer came that proved that the call was from God."

As the sun set against their backs that evening, David sensed a shadow had fallen across his friendship with Robert. His friend could not understand this call to go to foreign lands. By contrast, Robert insisted the field he was called to work in was the hay field out his back door.

Mary raised her eyebrows as she stood at the kitchen sink, looking out the window toward the barn. She watched Noah's gait as he came toward the porch door. It told her that he was in a hurry; probably with something important to say. She smiled to herself at how well she knew her husband.

Sure enough, Noah almost skipped into the kitchen, picked up a dish towel and began to dry the supper dishes. Not used to seeing her husband doing a domestic chore, Mary glanced his way and said, "Yes, what do you want?"

Noah chuckled. "What makes you think I want something?" he teased her. His tone reminded her of what made her fall in love with him so long ago. He had been a wild thing, using tobacco and rough language that betrayed his Brethren upbringing. But that was before he was truly converted.

"I'm sure there's some good reason why you decided to come back and help me with the dishes—and shoo the children away to do it!" she exclaimed.

"Well, Mary, you're right, as usual. Here it is: I feel called to travel around these states and tell the lost about our Lord Jesus."

"You mean you aren't content just telling our Kansas neighbors now? And what of me?" Mary asked.

"You'll come with me of course," he answered.

"The children?" Mary asked.

"The oldest ones are old enough to watch over the rest," Noah assured her.

"Now, I'm not sure about that," she countered. "I'll have to do some praying over this."

"You do that, Mary. I know the Lord will answer," Noah said and laid down his towel–next to a rack of still–wet dishes.

"Wait, we're not finished here," Mary said, trying to hide her small smile.

"Let them air dry," Noah replied, sprinting off toward the door. As the screen door banged shut, Mary laughed aloud. Life with Noah Zook was certainly never dull! She let her mind wander back to 1872, when Noah surprised her soundly by announcing he felt called to the ministry.

In 1881, she happily packed up their Franklin County, Pennsylvania homestead and together, they built a new life on a farm in Dickinson County, Kansas. They were among almost 300 men, women and children of their Brethren who had made the move to this beautiful valley near Abilene, where farm soil was rich and selling for as little as $7 an acre. By comparison, many had sold their land at home for $130 or more an acre. By Kansas standards, they were rich! Mary laughed at that thought; the only reason they valued money was to have more of it to support foreign missions!

Jesse Engle scanned the numbers on the page until they threatened to blur. He felt a familiar throbbing headache coming on. No matter how many times he scrutinized the numbers, the result was the same: There wasn't enough money to pay what he owed.

He sighed deeply and ran his hand through his thick head of hair. As he brought his hand down in front of his face, he paused and stared at it. It was a large, strong hand, calloused from hard farm work. Yet it was also a gentle hand, one that had reached out to comfort many a brother or sister since he had become an elder in the Kansas Brethren in Christ church. And it was the same hand that had extended fellowship to those Brethren who followed him from Pennsylvania to Kansas years earlier when he led that migration to a new land.

He was well-respected, he knew that. Perhaps that's why so many of the Brethren had trusted his idea to purchase a tract of land to be used for an orphans' home for widows and children. It had seemed like such a grand ministry and much needed when the Kansas Council of 1879 had approved the idea. The people gave him money toward a down payment to purchase the land; the rest was put on a mortgage, thereby putting the church in considerable debt with a high rate of interest. A loan was taken to aid that situation, yet it proved to only plunge them further into financial trouble. Crop harvests had been disappointing, and so Jesse had not been able to pay anything on the principal of the loan, barely scratching out enough to pay the interest.

Now, he knew what was on the horizon. He feared that he would be censured in some way for his financial failings when it came to the managing of the situation—and those fears proved true.

He stood with his head bowed at a special council meeting this cold February day. He heard the words and received them with shame: "As the nature of Brother Engle's failure is such as to concern brethren and outsiders in the loss of money and Christian confidence, it is resolved to revoke his service as Elder and minister."

That night as he sat in the privacy of his home, he allowed the tears to fall. "Oh Lord," he prayed, "Forgive me. I have always sought to do your will. Will I now and forever be remembered only as the foolish farmer who lost the church's money?"

Had the two men talked, David Zook might have taken comfort in knowing Jesse Engle was also wrestling with the opinion of the Brethren.

As David became more convinced that he was called to missions, he knew too that many in the small farming community, and indeed his own Zion Brethren in Christ (BIC) congregation, had grave reservations about his intentions to travel to Tabor, headquarters of the Hepzibah Faith Missionary Association, a school focused on holiness and foreign missions.

It was through his father, Noah, that David even knew of the place. A visiting missionary from Hepzibah had spent the night at their home and filled David's head with the visions of being surrounded by self-denying, plain people who discarded all entrapments of this life and spent much time in prayer with a true spirit of humility. Some people thought the Hepzibah missionaries were peculiar.

David took comfort in knowing his parents would understand. He knew his father was impressed with the Hepzibah people and had felt blessed by them after he visited there. So, with passion in his eyes that only hinted at that in his heart, David told his parents that he felt called to foreign soils to tell the message of Christ. His father seemed at first more accepting than his mother. "Mother," David told her, "I cannot deny what the Lord is asking of me-to assume my responsibility and go tell the Good News in places far from here!"

It would not be the last time that Mary would hear such passionate words about a life's calling to missions from one of her children. In fact, she would hear it four more times in the years to come.

Clifford Cress was busy working in the fields when he heard about the religious meetings to be held that night in the Zion BIC Church. The year was 1894.

They said David Zook, one of Noah's sons, was home from his trip to the Hepzibah Faith Missionary Association and believed himself to be called as a missionary to India. There was a big buzz about it all over the small farming community, where the thought of traipsing across the world to tell others about Jesus was as foreign an idea as India itself!

Clifford, always curious, decided he would go. He finished his barn work, put on clean clothes and combed himself. (In fact, he combed himself twice, figuring that such a holy meeting might draw some of the prettiest, most wholesome girls in the county!)

As he pulled his buggy into the dirt parking lot outside the church, he was surprised that space was at a premium. It seems he wasn't the only one curious to see what David Zook had to say.

Inside, the church was stuffy and the air stagnant, as Clifford sat waiting for the service to begin. Suddenly, without fanfare, David Zook took to the small wooden pulpit at the front of the church and exclaimed "What is keeping YOU from taking God's word out into the world?"

For more than an hour, David laid out his case for why Christians were compelled by the good Lord Himself to carry the salvation message far from their comfortable home. Sweat poured down his face as he attempted to convince his audience, which included many of his peers and just as many of his elders. At points it seemed his voice would give out entirely, and Clifford had to strain to hear him. Then suddenly, David's voice would boom out in full force, as if the Lord himself had breathed sound back into the young man's vocal chords.

At one point, Clifford noticed many of David's siblings were nodding their heads in agreement with what their brother had to say. His eye settled on pretty Sara Zook, David's younger sister. He momentarily became distracted from the message, but David's loud preaching soon brought his attention back around.

When he got home, Clifford found his own heart stirred by the words he had heard. Would God call a country farmer like himself to such a great task? Always one who loved to write, Clifford sat down to record his thoughts in his journal so he would never forget how he felt this very night. "David's zeal and preaching created a tremendous excitement among our quiet country people who were God-fearing farmers," he wrote. "They were fighting drought, chick bugs and Hessian flies in their fields and being buffeted by the prairie. Now to be called to assume a responsibility for saving the world, and dedicating their children and their substance to home and foreign enterprises never dreamed of, was way too much."

Clifford wrote of how David put "a new ideal" and "an awful fear of God" into their hearts. The meetings went on for ten nights, but Clifford didn't attend them all.

And so it was with interest that Clifford read David's own record of the events in the next issue of *Evangelical Visitor*, the Brethren in Christ Church periodical. "Many were at the altar and sought to have everything taken away that would hinder them in receiving the baptism of the Holy Ghost," David wrote.

In some ways, Clifford mused, the meetings had taken on a life of their own beyond those nights.

Some said David displayed miraculous healing powers. Clifford wished he had been able to go to more of the meetings to see for himself what all the commotion was about, but he had heard the rumors–that some people claimed they were healed when David touched them. David, for his part, said any cure was from the Lord, not his hand.

When David made his intentions known to leave for India, via Japan, Clifford was sorry that he couldn't rearrange his schedule to attend the farewell service held at the depot. But, he heard, twenty-five of the Brethren were there, even though David was not being sent by their denomination. "Well," he said aloud to himself, "That seems to matter not. Our people are behind the missions effort!"

All this made Clifford scratch his head and ponder anew whether God was calling him to service. He wasn't the only one. Eventually twenty-one young people from their cluster of Kansas churches, including Sara and Clifford, would find themselves on the foreign mission field.

Jesse Engle furrowed his brow. It was the last day of General Conference 1894, and he was ready to get home. His mind was tired from all it had been mulling over.

Then, suddenly, Mrs. Rhoda Lee, a fairly new member of the denomination sprang to her feet and, much to Jesse's surprise, to the podium of General Conference to speak.

Oh boy, here we go, Jesse thought to himself.
There will be no getting home very soon now.
Mrs. Lee was known for her many submissions to
the *Evangelical Visitor.* Jesse always read them
with interest because, unlike other female
contributors who focused on issues of common
opinion, such as the need for personal submission
to Christ or temperance, Rhoda's writings sought
to shake the Brethren out of their complacency
toward foreign missions. And the way she wrote
could make a person feel guilty indeed if he were
to ignore her words!

"I wish, by the help of God, to place before
our minds today, a few facts concerning our
obligations as stewards of God to obey our
Master's command to preach the gospel to every
creature," Rhoda Lee began.

Jesse drew in his breath. He had to admit that
he admired Rhoda's courage, even if he questioned
the propriety of her actions. Imagine a woman so
bold as to speak on the conference floor!

"Our Father sent His Son and the Son said, 'As
my Father hath sent me, even so send I you.' 'Go
ye therefore and teach all nations.' 'Go ye into all
the world and preach the Gospel to every
creature.'" She paused, "Are we true to the trust
He left us? Let us not trifle with so great a charge.
If we believe in the Great Commission, if we
believe in the Lord's Prayer, the Apostle's Creed,
the Beatitudes, the Coronation, it is high time for
us to awaken out of sleep–for the Lord is at hand."

Everyone sat motionless, as if stupefied by the
magnitude of what she said. Jesse scratched his
beard, a nervous habit.

Rhoda cleared her throat; she wasn't done. Next, she listed off what other church denominations were doing toward such work–the Baptists had raised $600,000, the Presbyterians over $1 million, the Lutherans in Kansas alone raised more than $4,000 for foreign missions. Jesse had to admit that Rhoda had his attention.

"Oh may I dare to hope that a missionary fund may be started and a systematic method of foreign work be organized, and that each of us will practice economy and self–denial to swell the fund?" she proclaimed. "The King's business requires haste, and may God speed the time when I hear a rumor from the Lord that an ambassador is sent among the heathen!"

Should he make a motion on this, Jesse wondered to himself, yet something held him back. Perhaps it was the memory of the orphanage effort gone bad. True, his own brothers and sisters in Christ had volunteered money to pay back his indebtedness, and he had been fully pardoned and restored in his ministry, but he had not forgotten his ill judgment and now shied away from entrepreneurial efforts. Jesse let the moment pass.

Later in the day, just when Jesse was thinking that conference business might wrap up in time for him to get home for supper, his thoughts were suddenly interrupted when he caught sight of Elder Jacob E. Stauffer out of the corner of his eye. Jesse's mouth fell open quite involuntarily as he watched Jacob stride forward intently, clutching a $5 bill in his hand. *What in the world?* Jesse thought, not taking his eye off his fellow brother.

Stauffer's footsteps echoed in the room–it was that quiet as he approached the conference table. Jesse watched in amazement as his friend laid the money down and said, "This is for Brethren in Christ foreign mission work." Immediately Rhoda Lee stood up, seized a fellow's hat and began passing it through the audience to receive an offering for foreign mission work. Jesse was so frazzled he didn't have time to think about whether to pass the hat or scrounge in his pockets for money. He began to pass it and then, at the last moment, pulled it back to make a small contribution. All the while, no one spoke or even moved in their seats, or so it seemed to Jesse.

The room was spellbound by the magnitude of what was happening. There was money now for a foreign mission work; that much could not be ignored. Before conference ended, there was a new Foreign Mission Fund, of which Stauffer was appointed treasurer.

Truth be known, Jesse was relieved that he had not been appointed treasurer, and somewhat chagrined, wondering if it had anything to do with his own failed finances. So it was with some hesitation that he accepted the position of secretary of the Foreign Mission Board the following year when, at conference, it was decided that there was reason enough to expand the board to twelve members.

It was Jesse's name that appeared in an appeal in the *Visitor* in 1897. Donations toward foreign mission work were to be sent to Jesse, and he would keep an account of the money and hand it over to the treasurer.

"Is this to be my only part in this endeavor, Lord?" Jesse wondered in his prayers. "Or do you have more for me to do in foreign missions?"

The hour was late, and the Calcutta streets had grown quiet. David was bone tired, but he knew he owed his parents and his supporters back home some long overdue correspondence. His wife, Katie, slept soundly in the bed near his writing desk. He gazed at her, smiled, and again thanked God for sending him such an able partner in life. He knew the minute he beheld her lovely face while at Tabor that this woman was God's gift to him. Katie was lively and smart, thoughtful and compassionate, and shared his zeal and courage for a life devoted to missions. Their first missions effort – two years of work together in Japan, evangelizing among the merchant and men-of-war ships in the harbor – had proved he was right about her.

"May 5, 1898" David wrote at the top of his letter. "Dear friends, I write to you from our new home in Calcutta, India. Since coming here, God's call upon our lives has only been reinforced . . . .Our hearts are filled with sadness while gazing upon these scenes of heathenism. Wherever we go, we see about us sin, sin, sin. But the worst part about it is that it is dragging souls down to Christless graves by the millions!"

Calcutta was no place for the faint of heart–or purpose. India's most populated city accommodated enough disease and poverty to dishearten even those sure they were called there by the Almighty! Yet David would not succumb to discouragement, not over the state of the people there and not over the difficult challenge of learning Bengali, the state dialect. Never one to waste opportunity, he set about evangelizing the students in the English-speaking universities in the cities in the meantime.

Money was another worry that threatened to discourage David. He was used to living simply, so the idea of signing on with the Hepzibah Faith Mission hadn't troubled him. The association was founded on faith; supported purely by freewill offerings. Sometimes it took a lot of faith to live that way, especially when it looked like it would take a lot of money to realize his dream of starting an orphanage in Calcutta. His letters home to the Visitor, he decided, would always include encouragement for the Brethren to support his work with donations. He found his pleas were not ignored and he thankfully received a good amount of support from the Brethren throughout his time in India.

Mary and Noah were named as traveling missionaries within the United States in 1888 by the Brethren in Christ General Conference, which made evangelizing all the more important in their hearts. They had already been traveling unofficially in the name of the Lord; now it was in

the name of the denomination too. They made it
part of their daily prayers to remember the
natives in India and to ask the Lord Almighty to
lift the veil from their eyes that they might see
Him as their Savior—and quick!

They also were happy to do what they could
to raise funds for their son's missionary
endeavors during their own evangelistic
campaigns on the home front. David had not gone
out under the auspices of the Brethren in Christ.
However, they reasoned, he was one of them and
the Brethren should be happy to support him.

Mary often turned to prayer for missionary
efforts at home and abroad, and was happy to
report regularly in the *Evangelical Visitor* about
their evangelistic journeys.

"What wonderful things the Lord has done for
many of the dear children of God; it is indeed
marvelous!" Mary wrote. "The refining fire has
surely been going through many hearts. Oh such
wonderful testimonies! Such cleaning up; such
filling with the Holy Ghost; such wonderful results
of divine healing! Oh how wonderful! How
marvelous! We are more than ever convinced that
this leading out is of the Lord."

CHAPTER TWO

THE CALL COMES

The Year 1897

Frances Davidson's heart was happy that wintry Kansas afternoon as she tidied up her small room in the boarding house near McPherson College where she taught. She had just the day before talked with other members of the faculty, giving her verbal agreement to remain teaching there for some years. Any restlessness she felt earlier had disappeared with the commitment to stay on. She did love teaching, and it seemed God had given her this opportunity for a stable, fulfilling job.

As she went for the day's mail, she was glad to see it contained the newest copy of the *Evangelical Visitor* – January 15, 1897. She always enjoyed keeping up with the news among the Brethren. She opened the cover to an appeal from Samuel Zook, who was now treasurer of the Mission Board: "We would call attention to the fact that the committee appointed at last Conference is ready to act on the foreign mission work, but up to this time they have received no applications. Why is this? Does the Lord not speak to some hearts? Or is it because the Church is not praying the Lord of the harvest to send laborers into His field?"

Frances's heart caught in her chest. She went on to read Zook's praise for the self-sacrificing spirit of the missionary, who cuts loose from his own life to follow God's call. He urged readers who may think the Lord was calling them to reply, "Lord, thy servant heareth!"

All evening, Frances couldn't shake those words 'Thy servant heareth' from her mind. "Why am I thinking about this?" she asked herself when she awoke in the middle of the night. "I have no thought of foreign mission work! I just agreed to stay here!"

The next day, however, in the midst of reading students' exams, a vivid picture came into her mind. She saw herself sitting at her desk and she saw the Lord sweep all other books from her desk, save the Bible. She breathed hard and blinked. "Are you calling me, Lord, me?" she whispered and felt the overwhelming assurance that, yes, He was calling her.

Determined that she would not tarry, she went immediately to the dean of her school and told him of her intentions. "The Lord has filled me with an unutterable love for every soul who has not heard of him, and with a passionate longing to go to the worst parts of the earth, away from civilization, away from other mission bodies, and spend the rest of my life in telling the story of the Cross," she said with great emotion.

The older man rubbed his chin—who could argue with that, he thought—and gave his young teacher his blessing to go.

Frances Davidson's father, Henry Davidson, former editor of the church periodical and chairman of the missions board, had much the same reaction. "How can I say yes, and how dare I say no?"

Not far from where Frances was digesting her newfound calling, Jesse Engle was struggling with the same. He knew he had received a call to spread the Gospel when still a young man, but with no encouragement and no means to do so, he had slowly let that urging recede to the back of his mind. All this talk of the new missions effort in his own denomination however had it all bubbling back to the surface. He thought he felt it again–this call to foreign missions–but he couldn't for the life of him figure out why God would call one as old as himself. Nearly sixty he was! Surely there must be others younger and more capable, he whispered to the Lord, but he felt no release from the thoughts in his mind.

Once certain, he approached his dear wife, Elizabeth. She did not attempt to deflate him. "My place is beside you," she said. "Where you go, I will follow." Jesse was profoundly grateful for her support, and next sought the blessing of his children. "It is hard to say why such a wonderful event should take place," he told them. "After having emerged from great trials of faith and having had prospects of a happy, peaceful life in old age, that we should respond to a call, which seems almost presumptuous for someone my age, and formally break the ties of a blessed family union, can only be understood by Him who claims the rectorship of our being, glory to His name!"

The children were supportive, though hesitant. "I know you would much rather your father live out his

days in the rocking chair in the old farmhouse,"
Jesse joked, and then turned serious. "Not knowing
what a day will bring forth or what our earthly future
will be, my dear children, by God's grace I will
promise you that we have always aimed at your
greatest happiness, most especially for eternity. Our
warmest affections shall continue 'til life shall ebb
out its last breath and then hopefully look to the
'other shore' for a blessed reunion."

There were tears all around, bittersweet tears
shed by a family close at heart and close to God,
and now soon to be countries apart.

"Sara," Noah called his daughter from the
kitchen to join him in the parlor of their modest
farmhouse. "I have asked Clifford to spend an
evening with us next week when he is home for a
visit. I have a very serious matter to discuss with
him. I want you to hear about it first."

Sara's heart leapt in her chest. She thought
she knew what was coming, having been prepared
for the possibility by her gentle mother who
wished only to reassure her of her future. Still,
her father's serious tone made her doubt for a
moment.

"Your mother and I see that you and your
siblings are growing and becoming more
independent everyday. You know our hearts have
always longed for more time to share the Gospel
with those who have not heard it. So your mother
and I are set on asking your young man . . ."

At the mention of "your young man," Sara smiled involuntarily. Clifford was her man, wasn't he! The thought of it still set her heart thumping. Yes, they were betrothed, even as he toiled as a school teacher in Tabor, Iowa, closer to her brother, Eber, who was studying there, than to his own beloved. But all that could be about to change.

". . . to lease this home and dairy on a five-year contract," Noah was finishing his sentence as Sara shook away her own thoughts.

"Here? With me?" she nearly shouted.

"Yes, daughter, here, with you," her father agreed. Sara threw her arms around her father and hugged him tightly. The Zooks, unlike some of the more reserved Brethren, did not hesitate to show their heartfelt affection.

Their wedding was simple, held in the same room where Sara first heard the news of her father's offer. Life began for Mr. and Mrs. G. Clifford Cress with a fully-equipped dairy farm, forty head of cattle and the promise of a happy future. Sadness lay just ahead for the newlyweds however. Twice within the first several years of marriage, Sara gave birth to a baby who died shortly afterwards. Sara and Clifford held strong to their faith, though, and remained convinced that their life would one day revolve around a farm table full of children and a barn full of high-producing dairy cows.

Yet Sara knew that her young husband was wrestling with a mighty question: Should he continue with the farming life that had fallen in their laps seemingly as a gift from God as well as from Sara's parents? Or should he forsake all this and take his new bride to a foreign land to preach the word of God to those lost in spiritual darkness?

As for Sara, she was willing to do whatever the Lord asked of her and her husband. Ever since she accepted the Lord as her Savior at age nine, she had felt an increasing desire to allow her life to be shaped by Him.

The answer for their future plans came to young Clifford one day in the fall of 1897. He suddenly felt convinced that, yes, if a way should open for missionary service, they would take it. Sara was in agreement.

Mary and Noah were not surprised when the afternoon mail brought word that their new son-in-law intended to break his farming contract with them and partner with God in the business of saving souls.

The baby birds chirping in a nest outside Eber Zook's window this early spring morning seemed to be singing just for him. Life was beginning anew on the Kansas prairie, and in Eber's soul as well. The fourth son of Noah and Mary Zook was about to start down the path forged by his older brother before him. Eber was taking his new bride, Amanda, and setting sail for India to work side by side with his brother David.

Today was Sunday and Eber was preparing for services, but this was not just any Sunday morning service. His hands shook slightly as he reread the

flier announcing the service—April 3, 1898—
Consecration Service for Four Brothers and Sisters
in Christ Called from Among Us to Foreign Mission
Work. He would be consecrated for service along
with his wife, Amanda, his sister Sara and her new
husband, Clifford. His parents, he knew, were
overflowing with joy that two more of their children
had been called by God to this special work.

Mary Zook was lost in her own thoughts this
same morning as she dressed for Sunday service.
Her mind kept going back to the tiny babe her son
Eber had once been.

"Mother?" Noah's voice sounded in the hall,
and he stepped into their bedroom and smiled at his
wife. "I wondered if you were overcome—you've
been in here so long!"

"I am remembering," she said, fastening her
covering with a straight pin in her hair. "Do you
remember how Eber was so small—his face was
the size of a teacup? How we carried our frail
little boy around on a pillow for months?"

Noah grinned, "Indeed, I do. The doctor said
he would not live. Now look at him—strong and
ready to sail to another land!"

"And do you remember, Noah, when he was
only seven, how he told us that his heart was
beating very, very fast when he decided to stand
up and accept the Lord? It seemed he really knew
what he was doing," Mary said, smiling faintly.
"He always did say he was ready to serve God
wherever He called."

"And now he will carry this important message
across the seas, Mother," Noah said. "God has
surely blessed our little boy Eber!"

The church was nearly full when Noah and Mary entered and parted company in the aisle. The ladies sat on one side, their head coverings forming a sea of white caps across the rows. The men, bearded and pensive, sat on the other side. The elders sat behind a table at the front of the meeting house. After worship and a charge to the young missionaries given by the bishop, all four came forward and knelt before the pulpit.

The room was still. The ministers, along with Noah and Mary and the other parents, laid their hands on their children's heads as a prayer was spoken over them.

Oh, how full was Mary's heart with the joy of having birthed so many children intent on bringing glory to their Heavenly Father! As of yet, Mary did not know that her joy would soon turn to mourning.

It was 3 a.m., but Rhoda Zook was wide awake. Her eyes scanned the ceiling of the small room she called hers while she completed her studies at the Hepzibah Faith Mission. She wished she had a nickel for every time she had said, "Yes, I'm David's little sister," to people at the mission. Like her brother, now so far away in India, Rhoda too was feeling drawn to foreign missions.

"Well, this certainly isn't the first time I've been awakened in the middle of the night," Rhoda thought as her eyes adjusted to the darkness in the room. When she was growing up, many a night she felt the Lord Himself woke her and spoke to her soul, urging her toward salvation. Then, she had resisted. Even at age eleven when she joined the church, she didn't really know what salvation was, she later realized. She chuckled as she recalled what she had later told her mother about her experience, "If one goes down in the water a dry sinner, he will only come up a wet one! It's the blood of Jesus Christ alone that can cleanse one from sin!"

That saving knowledge had come for Rhoda not a moment too soon. "I was so miserable in my sins that I was glad to say yes to His voice and obey Him at any cost," she had explained to her parents when telling them of her life-changing conversion. "I have real peace in my soul—the peace that passeth understanding!"

It was that peace she urged her parents to pray for when she told them she felt called to go to Tabor to work only for God. She later recorded her experience in the church periodical. "Many thought it strange and feared I was being led by some spirit other than God's," she had written. "I have found it so grand to trust God for everything, and He has so graciously supplied all my needs, and I thank Him for it. . . . I do not know where God will yet lead me, but I have settled it in my heart to follow Him all the way, even though He takes me to the darkest corner of the earth to shine for Him."

And here she was, wide awake in a strange bed, listening again for God's instructions. Her mind immediately went to the man she had met while here in Tabor, Josiah Martin, who hailed from Elizabethtown, Pennsylvania. Also trying to make sense of a call to missions, Josiah had found a fast friend in Rhoda. Soon the pair were spending many hours together, talking about much more than missions.

Rhoda sighed, "What of this man, Lord?" she whispered. "I had committed myself to you, Lord. Can I yet commit myself to a husband?" The answer came in the form of a familiar peace that passed over her being and settled in her heart. There it was again; that peace that passes understanding. It was enough. Rhoda closed her eyes and slept until first light.

CHAPTER 3
FIRST STEPS

The Year 1898

Seven months had gone by since Jesse and Elizabeth Engle, Frances Davidson, Alice Heise and Barbara Hershey left America by ship on November 24, 1897 to sail to Cape Town for their ultimate destination in the interior of Africa.

With thoughts of America on her mind on the evening of July 4, Frances Davidson joined her traveling companions in the back of a donkey wagon to begin the two-day trip to Matopo. She was extremely grateful to the Seventh Day Adventist missionary who had offered them passage to their new home, which was 3,000 acres in the Matopo Hills of Southern Rhodesia. How they got the land was a story in and of itself, Frances chuckled to herself. Who would have thought that Cecil John Rhodes, instrumental in taking this land for the British, would meet Brother Jesse and willingly give him some of that land—and a letter for government officials advising the same? Mr. Rhodes had made peace with the natives and gained their trust. Though he was no religious man himself, he thoroughly believed in missionary work among the people. Frances sent up a prayer once again, thanking God for His perfect timing and praying for safe haven in their new land. It was home to the Matabele people, a branch of the Zulu tribe of Southeast Africa.

The group traveled best at night, by moonlight, after the heat of day had passed. As she listened to the clip‑clop of eighteen donkeys that pulled their wagon full of supplies, Frances gazed at the endless African sky and was nearly overcome with excitement over what lay ahead. It was a terribly long trip, seeing that the donkeys went about two miles an hour. At one point, the group despaired when the wagon got stuck in a swamp. The next day, with the help of natives, they loosed it and were again on their way.

On the morning of July 7, they arrived at their new home. Frances, ever one to record things in her journal, took up her pen and wrote: "There, spread out before our eyes, was a beautifully rolling valley of rich, dark earth, well supplied with an abundance of fresh water. I want never to forget this sight; this day."

The chief of the natives had called a meeting right away to introduce the new travelers. "These are not like other white people," he told them. (Frances and the others heard these words through an interpreter.) "They have come to teach you and your children and to do you good." Many heads nodded in understanding. Frances smiled. Acceptance seemed imminent.

Jesse Engle flinched just a little as his feet hit the cold water. He smiled broadly at the ten men who stood by on shore. *Thank you, oh Lord,* he prayed silently, *thank you for blessing our efforts;*

thank you for the testimony of these men who give us hope that our efforts will bear fruit.

"Come, let us baptize you into new life in Christ," he said, motioning for the first man to step into the water.

Jesse couldn't stop the tears of joy that rolled down his cheeks as he dunked the last man underwater.

He recalled the words of the letter he had written to his children as he traveled toward his foreign post. "We have no reason to doubt our calling to this mission. The nearer we approach the field, the more I am convinced of that. And the more I become acquainted with the real condition of Africa, the more I feel it has been the field into which the Lord has called us. What the future will develop, we do not know, nor do we care. We care only that we are in the order of the Lord."

The Lord had indeed shown them His care, in every step since they disembarked from the ship. Jesse himself was well pleased that he had been able to secure this land from Cecil Rhodes. He thought over their first week there, when they laid tentative plans for all they hoped to accomplish in the first month. The first order of business was the building of mud huts. That left their tent free for church services and school. Jesse laughed at the memory of the first day of school, when fifteen nearly naked children showed up at the tent to study. A sewing school was started promptly!

"Oh Lord, you are a marvel," Jesse said to himself as he waded out from the water. "Thank you for using me in this wondrous work!"

"Eber, it's as if you are getting all your practice in now!" Amanda Zook teased her new husband as they sailed from New York City enroute to India in October 1898.

Eber laughed. "I suppose the more practice, the better!" It was true, he had been perhaps a little over zealous as he held daily services aboard the ship and told any who would listen that their souls needed saving.

Ever since he sensed a call from the Lord, Eber had been anxious to join his brother in what appeared to be ever-expanding work in India. Now, finally, he and Amanda were headed there to make a difference, they hoped.

And they were not disappointed. The very summer after he and Amanda arrived, the brothers initiated orphanage work for destitute children and widows. Next came a school through which the children could get not only religious training but also learn a trade such as carpentry or agriculture. Though they started out with only four orphans, by August of 1900, there were 150 children.

David and Eber wrote a plea that would appear in the *Visitor*, asking for funds to purchase a larger residence. The Brethren came through with enough money to purchase a three-acre lot capable of housing 300 children.

Eber happily composed a letter to the church paper back home, describing the brothers' excited reaction to the gift. "The cash has been paid and we have the clear papers to this land and now we

push our building operations as fast as circum-
stances will allow and God orders," he penned.

"Are you going to describe our living quarters,
brother?" David inquired as he saw Eber busy
writing. "It's quite the story!"

Eber nodded and began to write about the
thirteen-feet-square hut they called home, with
walls of mats made from the bark of a tree and a
flat roof of poles, rice-straw and brush. "We are
quite snug, but our house is strictly a dry-
weather one. We do not expect rain for a few
months, as this is the dry, cool season."

"Are you going to mention that we sleep on the
ground and sit on the ground, save a few sun-dried
bricks that we've fashioned to sit upon?" David
said with a smirk. "Makes the hard church benches
back home seem mighty comfortable, not?"

Eber laughed and cast his brother a knowing
look. The two brothers delighted in each other's
company and in the fact that they worked so well
together. What one knew or thought, it seemed
the other knew or thought too; so it was easy to
work together harmoniously. Much was being
done for the Lord, and Eber felt a special place in
his heart for the dear children with whom he
spent so much of his time. The children returned
his love, calling him *"choto papa,"* which meant
Little Papa.

Eber also delighted in passing out tracts to
anyone he met, from a student at the university to
a beggar on the street. "Any soul is worth
saving!" he would exclaim. "We are surrounded
by people in nearby villages who have not heard

the saving message of Christ. Oh, it is awful to contemplate, especially when one considers that Jesus has fully paid the ransom price of every one of them!"

Eber dated his letter, November 29, 1900, and sent it off to be posted. Never did he think it would be the last he would write.

"We will sail from New York aboard the White Star liner 'Majestic' on the eighth of March," Sara told her parents. The year was 1899, and the future lay before these two young missionaries as vast and foreign as the waters over which they sailed to reach Port Elizabeth, Cape Colony.

It seemed that Clifford and Sara felt called to evangelize amidst the Matabele in Rhodesia, South Africa; to join the first missionaries from the Brethren in Christ—Jesse Engle among them. It warmed Mary's heart to know that her precious Sara would be among such godly men as Elder Jesse Engle. It gave her some measure of reassurance also that her young daughter, just twenty-three, and son-in-law seemed so filled with confidence and joy at the prospect of traveling to such a barren land.

Once in Rhodesia, Sara and Clifford sent word home about their new surroundings, and about the Matabele, in particular. Clifford described them as a "powerful tribe" filled with witch doctors and wizards and bizarre practices such as putting to death innocent people whom they suspected of causing anything from a sick cow to a drought. The Matabele were prone to strong drink, stealing and lying. To Mary Zook, it sounded like a terrifying place to be. To Sara and Clifford, it felt safe because they were convinced that it was exactly where God wanted them to be.

"But this love which constrains a man or a woman to give his or her life to this work, does much to relieve all disagreeable relations, and you see through their filth and repulsive manners, souls that ought to be saved and whose salvation depends largely on your efforts," Clifford wrote home. "Then you forget all the hindrances and serve there with gladness, knowing your Master endured much to save and redeem you."

Sara did her best to make their little hut beneath a large breadfruit tree at the Matopo Mission as homey as she could. Life was busy with language study, regular services at the mission station, and teaching and preaching in the villages and at the mission school.

"Soon we will be moving to a new station in Entabeni," she wrote home to her parents. "We will walk the one and a half hours between the two stations." Their hut of a home there, she wrote, was marred by soaking rains, and she did not expect the floor to solidify until the rain stopped. To make matters worse, the area was thick with white ants that ate everything, even their shoes! Mary shuddered to think of the living conditions of her daughter, but Sara's letters bore no hint of homesickness, only excitement at what God was doing.

One afternoon, as Sara was cheerfully going over her language lessons in their humble hut, Clifford came in, visibly shaken. "What is it, my love?" Sara asked at once, dropping her papers to come alongside her pale husband. "Are you sick?"

"No, no," Clifford replied, as if in a daze. "I just had the strangest . . . thought . . . or dream, though I am fully awake," he stammered.

"What? What was it" Sara implored him with a furrowed brow.

"It was . . . it was that you, that you will . . . die," he said, and cast his wife a most sorrowful glance. "And that I will return to America alone."

CHAPTER FOUR
THE ULTIMATE COST

The Year 1900

M ary carried all good thoughts of her children in her head and sent up prayers daily for their safety and their ministry.

Her heart felt especially light as she received the news from Rhoda that she and her beau Josiah planned to be married in the spring and then travel to India to serve in foreign mission work there.

She had already suspected as much, judging from the way Rhoda went on and on about Josiah in her letter from Tabor. Mary was glad not only that her daughter had found love, but that she had found someone as passionate about serving God as she. And, Mary noted, now Rhoda would have a strong, able man to protect her in the far-off land of India.

"May this be a good year, Lord," Mary prayed one January morning as she and Noah shared their daily reading of the Bible together over a breakfast of scrapple, dried beef hash and black coffee. Noah squeezed her hand in agreement.

In fact, this would turn out to be the hardest year of Noah and Mary Zook's life.

Sara knew she didn't feel right. She was extremely hot all over and overcome with a fatigue that threatened to bring her to her knees.

"Clifford," she called out, seeing that her husband's spot in the bed was empty. "Clifford, I need you!"

Her husband rushed into the hut to her bedside and immediately touched his hand to her forehead and drew it back. "Dear God!" He exclaimed. "You are so very hot!"

Sara looked at his face, but it was fading in and out. Once, she thought she saw her father's sweet face and then again, it became her dear husband's face peering at her, then . . .

"Daddy?" she asked. "Daddy, get Mama. I need Mama."

Alarmed, Clifford tried to soothe his wife—"It's me, Darling; it's Clifford"—and then he hurriedly reached for a paper and pen to write an urgent note to be sent to Jesse Engle and the others. Send help, NOW, he wrote.

Frances watched the sun rise over the hills outside her window and felt drawn to start her day early. She never ceased to marvel at the view. An African sunrise seemed like none other she had ever seen—the colors streaked more vibrantly than she ever recalled in the States, across a seemingly endless sky. It was as if the Lord Himself swept a paintbrush across it.

"Ah, the third week of January already," she said aloud as she glanced at the calendar. She smiled as she recalled the memory of Sara's grin as she handed her the wrapped calendar at their

Christmas celebration just several weeks earlier. Sara had asked her mother to send calendars from the States and was eager to present them to each person, knowing Frances in particular would appreciate something so common yet so impossible to find in their new surroundings.

Just then, a messenger came running past her hut, yelling excitedly that he had news. Frances ran from her hut just as Jesse and Elizabeth emerged from theirs as well. The young boy thrust a note at Jesse. He skimmed it.

"Sister Cress is ill with fever," he said. "We must go to them."

By the time their convoy arrived at Entabeni Mission, they found Clifford now also burning with fever. The only thing they knew to do was bring them both to Matopo Mission and nurse them back to health.

"I do not think it is serious," Frances declared to Jesse after both husband and wife were put in beds in opposite ends of the same hut, with a heavy curtain hung between them. "The Lord has given us such wonderful health since we arrived. I think this will pass."

However, Sara's fever soon rose to 105 degrees and Clifford's temperature surpassed that to register 106 degrees. Frances and Jesse rarely left their sides.

For several days, Sara lay with fever, complaining of severe pain in her back. She was alternately delirious and lucid. She slipped into unconsciousness for twenty-four hours, and just when Frances began to wonder if she would ever

wake up, she opened her eyes and spoke.
"Please, pray for me, that I should recover well,"
she said. Then, she fell into a deep sleep once
again, but later that evening, she woke and asked
for food. Her fever was almost gone. Frances'
heart leapt for joy; surely, the worst was past.

"Sit down, dear Father Engle," Sara said,
smiling weakly at Jesse, who stood by her
bedside. "You will tire of standing by me."

"I am by you, dear sister," he said, pressing
his hand on her cheek. "And the Lord is by you,
do not forget that."

At the other end of the hut, Clifford still lay
with a fever of 104 degrees. As Sara enjoyed a
sip of grape juice, she asked whether her husband
might enjoy some as well. "Don't stint Clifford on
my account," she directed. "My love, are you
thirsty?"

Those were the last words Sara would say to
her beloved husband. Several hours later, she
abruptly breathed a final breath and passed into
eternity on February 8 at the young age of twenty-
six. Frances marked the date on her calendar.

"Sister Mary, I am so happy to meet you again.
I heard you and your husband speak in
Pennsylvania last year, and I never forgot what
you said about sacrificing all for the sake of the
cross. Your message liked to have changed my
life! Bless you!"

Mary Zook smiled at the woman who spoke
such warm words to her. Though she was bone

tired from days of revival services here in
Ontario, her heart was glad to hear that their
traveling and evangelizing efforts did bear fruit.

"Mary, Darling, it is a letter–from Matopo
Mission," Noah said, coming up beside her and
holding out a letter to her. Mary could see it was
opened, and then she noticed the tears streaked
across her husband's face just as he turned away
from her.

"Noah?" She rose and turned his face toward
hers for a better look.

"It is not good news," he said in a low voice,
and took her arm to lead her to a more private
room. "Mary, Sara has died from malarial fever."

Mary felt the room begin to spin. She moaned.
"Mary," Noah steadied her with his strong arms.
"Mary, it will be all right."

Later, after many tears and a prayer, Mary
was ready to read the letter from Frances that
described her daughter's last moments on earth. It
pained her to think that she had not been there,
offering a mother's loving comfort. "Once Sara
murmured something about the 'veil being taken
away,' and she was no doubt viewing eternity. . . .
She looked so beautiful and so peaceful with a
slight smile on her face. She was the brightest
and best of our number and yet the first taken."

Mary wondered how she could bear up under
the great grief that swept over her.

The Zooks' pain was shared by many among
the Brethren who knew Sara personally or had
read her reports of the happenings in Africa in the
pages of the *Evanglical Visitor*. It was there that

Mary and Noah chose to formally share their reaction to the dreadful news: "We do not understand just why such who are so young and well qualified for the work should be removed so early . . . Her letters came to us so frequently and were so full of good cheer and hope for the salvation of that clime."

Mary took comfort in reading one of the last things her daughter had written concerning her passion toward missions. In an entry titled "Hearts Set for the Field," in the June 1898 *Visitor*, Sara wrote of their definite call to be faith missionaries in Africa. Mary read again the hopeful verse with which Sara had closed her entry, "Our God and Father, while we stray far from home on life's rough way; Oh, teach us from our hearts to say, 'Thy will be done.' What tho' in lonely grief we sigh for friends beloved no longer nigh, submissive still would we reply, 'Thy will be done.' Then when on earth we breathe no more, the prayer oft mixed with tears before, we'll sing upon a happier shore, 'Thy will be done.'"

"Yes, Lord," Mary breathed, "Thy will be done. Forgive me that I cannot agree to it nor stop from questioning it. But yet I know it Lord; thy will be done."

Clifford suffered with the same malarial fever, even as a pine coffin was made for his wife and she was laid inside, in a bed of white muslin. Sara was buried under a breadfruit tree near the station, and still Clifford lay sick. It would be twenty-eight days before he could even sit up and compose a letter home.

"God has given me wonderful sustaining power. I did not see Sara for three days before she died, neither afterward, as I was too sick. What a stroke? What a trial? I feel like a poor, heartbroken child, and if I live, I am coming home," he penned. "I looked forward to years of labor among these mountains, but today finds me a sadly different man, almost wrecked by grief and fever."

Frances paced in her hut. She was ashamed at herself, yet she could deny it no longer. She was angry with God.

"Why did you allow this, Lord?" she finally spat out with a vehemence that surprised even herself. "Sara laid her all upon the altar for Africa. She wanted to spend her life on behalf of this people! She wanted nothing more than to shine for You!"

In the nine and a half months Sara had been with them, Frances reasoned, she had thrown her heart and soul into the work with the natives. Sara had learned the language with ease and taken every opportunity to share about God. She had recently organized a sewing class for the women, careful to instruct them not only about how to use a needle but how to use the Bible to sew a perfect fit in life.

"She was gifted, so gifted!" Frances exclaimed to no one but herself. "Why did You take her to Yourself, Lord? We needed her here!"

Frances wept. She cried for all the plans that she had shared with Sara, for all the years they would have spent together in this exciting land to which they both felt called by God. She cried for Clifford, for the grief she saw in his face as he praised God for his own healing yet wrestled with the reasons why God had not healed Sara. And Frances cried for herself, and for the hopeful spirit that seemed to take flight from her soul with Sara's last breath.

"Dear God," she prayed, "I don't want to feel like this. Forgive me. Please help me to accept Your way and, more than that, to shine for You once again with full confidence, though I do not understand."

Today is the day. I must begin. Clifford told himself this as he reached for a box of Sara's keepsakes. He knew he had to start going through her things, now that he was stronger. It made no sense to pack up everything and ship it home with him. He would weed out the precious mementos of his brief life with his beloved and leave the inconsequential things behind in Africa.

As he sifted through a box of letters, he came across an autograph album. In it was a letter written to him by Sara, on July 8, 1898. He opened it and felt a familiar stabbing pain in his heart at the sight of her handwriting. "My Precious Husband," it began. "Since God has laid His hand upon us, and brought us into the blessed relationship of husband and wife, how sweet has been our life . . . By and by, after the wide, heaving sea has passed beneath our feet, and we land on Africa's shores, and years–perhaps only months–have passed away behind us, it may be that the natives will stand in solemn groups, speaking in low tones in the language we love so well, and beckoning with sad faces toward our dwelling place among them. Then they will walk slowly away to a shady nook nearby and begin to make a grove. And they will say to one another *"Umfundise file"*–"our teacher is dead."

Clifford's heartbeat quickened as he read on: "Perhaps there is a little woman in the coffin, and a lonely man following in its sad train. But do not weep dear husband. Is not the strength of God sufficient for this trial?"

Was this a premonition? Suddenly Clifford recalled his own peculiar vision just several weeks earlier about his wife's death and his return to America. "Dear God," he prayed. "What does all this mean?"

Jesse Engle couldn't reconcile it in his mind. Why, he kept asking himself, why would the Lord take one so young and so willing as Sara? She had been so well received among the Matabele, so good at learning their language, so eager to spend her life leading souls to the Kingdom.

All these things he pondered in his heart as he made frequent trips back and forth to Bulawayo to carry out the beginning work of the mission. Sometimes it was pouring down rain as he went, yet still he forced himself onward.

"What of it all?" he asked himself frequently on such trips. "The Mission was in promising condition, when suddenly this gloom falls upon us. Our first new and promising Station is deserted at the opening of the bud. What shall we say?"

Jesse thought of Peter and the disciples, casting their net down in hopeless toil, with no fish in return. They were dejected, defeated, until they heard the sweet voice of their Lord calling to them from the shore. Jesse's heart skipped a beat, and then he finally felt the first strain of peace in his heart since Sara's death. He heard the words of Isaiah 40:31 in his mind: "Wait upon the Lord, for such shall renew their strength as doth the eagle; they even shall not faint, *though they be old.*"

There came a day in late March when Jesse could not deny his ill health any longer. He had a bad head cold, then a fever and spent several days in and out of bed.

When Sunday came, he asked Brother Cress to open services for him. "He is pale and has a weak voice and an uncertain step," Clifford remarked to Frances soon afterward. "I am worried."

Monday dawned and Jesse felt better, and told his fellow missionaries that he thought the worst was past. Clifford, due to go to Bulawayo on business, asked Jesse if he should still go. "Yes, go," Jesse told him, then, in a gush of emotion, he added, "Oh Brother Cress, my heart is overflowing with love to God. He seems so near me since I am sick and my body is weak!"

Not without some misgivings, Clifford got on his bicycle and rode ten miles to Ft. Usher, where he stopped to spend the night with a friend.

Little did he know that back home, Jesse had been overcome with a chill. He began to talk a blue streak in the Zulu language and then lapsed into a stupor. Later in the evening, a runner arrived with a note for Clifford, telling him that Jesse was worse and he should return home in the morning. Clifford slept fitfully that night and woke to more notes from the Mission instructing him to telegraph at once to Bulawayo for a doctor. Once that was done, Clifford pedaled his bike as fast he could back to the Mission, feeling with every mile the leftover fatigue from his own recent illness.

Clifford arrived home at noon and found Jesse in bed, his breathing labored and punctuated by moans.

"The sun was hanging low over Matopo's wild and rugged hills and the tall trees casting long pensive shadows across the valley when we gathered around Jesse's cot to witness the last sad event of a useful and well-spent life," Clifford later described the scene. "It came to us like a thunderbolt from clear skies."

As Jesse breathed his last, Elizabeth leaned over him and imprinted on his face a kiss for each of their seven sons back home in America. The scene was almost more than Clifford and the others could bear to watch.

Word was sent to the doctor, who was still about four miles out, not to come. Clifford suggested letting him come anyway to make an examination, but Elizabeth did not agree, so the matter was dropped.

As there was no lumber on hand, Clifford took down doors on their huts to fashion a coffin. Jesse was buried next to Sara. "We are brokenhearted, grieved, yea, astonished at the Providences of our adorable God," Clifford wrote, preparing a letter for the *Visitor*. "Our leader is gone; none of us can take his place. Yet, we all humbly submit and in Christ-like submission say, 'Thy will be done forever.' Amen."

Elizabeth stood at the burial site long after the others had left. Tears slipped down her cheeks as she ran her hand over the fresh earth. "Dear husband," she whispered. "At one time, you grieved that you would only be remembered as one who led the church into financial woe. Now, dear Jesse, you will always be remembered as the one who led the church into foreign missions. Praise be, dear one! You leave such a legacy!"

Shortly after this, Mother Engle came down with the African fever herself and was sick intermittently with fever for three months. It wasn't until mid-July that she was well enough to make the trip back home to America with Clifford, a widow and a widower returning home alone with nothing but the memory of their loved ones, buried under a breadfruit tree in Africa.

Mary and Noah tried to carry on their evangelistic work with the same hope and enthusiasm as ever. If Mary admitted the truth, however, Sara's death had tempered her enthusiasm for the moment. She even caught herself thinking at stray moments "if only" thoughts–if only Sara hadn't been called, if only she had stayed on the farm, if only she were still here . . . Mary knew the Lord's timing was perfect with her head–not always with her heart–these days. She thought often of her youngest daughter, Martha, who was in Illinois, preparing for mission service in Africa. She knew she must not worry for her safety but commit her to the Lord's protection as she had all her children.

So it was with great shock that Noah and Mary, who were conducting evangelistic services in Lancaster, Pennsylvania in July of that same year, once again received terrible news; this time it was Martha. She was dead from diphtheria at the tender age of seventeen.

"This comes like a thunderbolt upon us," Noah said, describing their feelings in the *Evanglical Visitor* upon hearing the news. "We were not even aware of her sickness." Yet, ever the trusting one, he added. "We do praise God that we do not mourn without hope, and we find the grace of God sufficient to bear us up."

In India, Amanda and Eber took the news of his sisters' deaths hard. They too wondered at God's plan, but tried with all their might to concentrate on the positive things God was doing through their work.

On one late December afternoon, Amanda readied supper with a light heart. Her beloved Eber was coming home from several days of preaching out in the countryside. He was doing that more and more now, as if the urgency to win souls for Christ was driving him harder and harder.

"My love, I'm home," Eber said, peeking his head in the doorway of their humble home. "And wait until I tell you about the beggar who asked Christ into his heart!"

"First, tell me how much you missed me!" Amanda said with a laugh and happily accepted a big hug from her husband.

After supper, Eber went right to bed, but Amanda didn't think much of it since his trip had been long. Over the next several days, he spoke of being weary, and Amanda urged him to get more rest. "The souls can wait; the children can wait," she said.

After several days, however, it was obvious that Eber was more than tired; he was sick.

"Eber, darling, may I get you some breakfast," Amanda inquired on the third morning of her husband's illness. "Come, can you sit up?" She threw back the covers to prepare to help him up when she gasped. Pox! Dear God, pox! Her soul cried out in fear, but her voice was steady: "Eber, we must pray! We must gather everyone and pray, dear heart. I'm afraid you have smallpox."

A look of alarm spread over Eber's face, then a calm. "Yes, Amanda, let us join in prayer. Surely the Lord has much left for me to do."

David and Katie and others in their small troop gathered together and prayed with such a might and a feeling that they were sure their brother would be healed. Eber himself, however, was not.

"Amanda," he said as the evening sun set over the hills near their home. "Are you willing to give me up?"

His young wife looked upon his handsome face, marred now by pox, yet endearing to her all the same. She remembered the first time she had looked into that face, kissed those lips, felt those eyes look deep into her soul . . . and she began to sob.

"Do not cry, do not worry!" Eber implored her. "If the Lord wants to take me, it will all just be glory!"

Seven days after he had turned ill, Eber died on December 18, 1900, leaving behind a devastated wife, a desolate brother and many grieving Indian orphan children who had lost their "Little Papa."

Amanda and David were with him when he passed. "David," Amanda whispered. "Can you feel it? When his spirit took flight, this room was filled with a heavenly host. I could feel their presence, I know it!"

Eber's remains were buried the next day in a nearby cemetery. None of the orphans were allowed to see Eber after he died because he was so disfigured from the pox. When they saw the small band of mourners returning from the cemetery, the children ran to Amanda and inquired as to Little Papa's whereabouts.

"My children, he has gone to meet the Lord in heaven," Amanda said, bending down to encircle them in a hug. The children immediately let out a pitiful, heart-piercing wail, which shook Amanda to her core.

There were many precautions to be taken to ensure no one else would contract the pox. Everyone was vaccinated, some things were disinfected and other things were burned. No one knew where Eber contracted smallpox, but Amanda felt sure that if it was the Lord's time to take Eber, it mattered not the cause; if not smallpox, then it would have been something else.

During the next month, Amanda's faith was tested as never before in her young life, but she found God was near and His grace was sufficient.

"This 'cup' has seemed as strongest vinegar mingled with bitterest gall, and even now it still seems hard to bear," Amanda wrote in a letter home. "But Jesus bore this sorrow and grief on the cross for me, and even now I know he is interceding of the Father on my behalf. What a wonderful Savior we have!"

David too was keenly aware of God's strong arms undergirding him in his grief. He penned a tribute for the *Visitor* to that end. "At such times as these, the Comforter is very precious. Praise the Lord! We are consecrated to stand by the work and be truer to God than ever before. Our prayer is that God will raise up someone to take the place quickly, and for the life of this young man, God would grant ten more."

"Mother, don't cry," Rhoda said, as she wrapped her arms around Mary Zook and held her close. "Our heartstrings are pained now, but I know your heart shares the joy of my heart, down deep, at what we are going to accomplish for God."

Mary nodded and wiped at a stray tear. She knew deep in her soul that what her daughter was doing was right; that it was to God's delight that Rhoda was giving up her secure life at home to bring news of His salvation to those in darkness across the ocean.

But she could not deny that a darkness had fallen across her soul at the very thought of it. And was it any wonder? Three times before Mary had unselfishly sent her children—though grown, always her babies—out to foreign lands. And now two already would not return. It took faith to send off a fourth child to an unknown land. Deep faith.

To ask Rhoda not to go would be nothing short of selfish—not to mention abundantly lacking in faith. To let her go was nothing short of torturous, and indeed it was only Mary's faith that allowed her to do it.

"Write to us as soon as you get there, or sooner!" she said, managing a small smile. "And Josiah, remind her if she forgets!" Her son-in-law smiled and assured her he would.

Rhoda and Josiah were set to leave New York on December 3, with hopes to reach Bombay, India just after the calendar turned to the new year of 1903.

This was their last time together at their Kansas farm before their departure. They had celebrated an early Christmas together. Would they ever celebrate another, Mary wondered and shuddered at the dark thought, trying to banish it to the recesses of her mind.

The Year 1904

"Just one year ago today we arrived here in India and truly it has been a grand year–the best of our lives!" Rhoda wrote, emphasizing the word "best" with an underline. She was preparing one of her frequent letters for publication in the *Evangelical Visitor*. She felt a great burden to let those at home know the wonderful things God was doing in India.

"We have started two Sunday Schools. We have met with some opposition, but we cannot think of stopping for that," she wrote. "This morning the natives had driven up their buffaloes to the place where we generally enter the village and seemingly thought they would keep us away by doing so, as the buffaloes are generally very vicious, especially toward white people. . . . But there is more than one way into the village, so going in another way, the Sunday School was held as usual, with 32 in attendance!"

Rhoda wrote passionately from her heart about their conviction that there was nothing more important or satisfying that dropping a seed of God's truth into the lives of these precious native children before their hearts were infested with superstition and a hardness toward the true God.

Evening was falling outside their small hut, and Rhoda smiled as Josiah gave her a wave and blew her a kiss as he passed by their humble home. He was on his way to have evening prayers with the boys of the village. He had been doing this since they arrived, and the boys had grown to love it.

"I don't know who enjoys it more, them or me," Josiah confessed when he shared with his wife how much joy there was in seeing the faith of these boys mature.

In their first meetings, it was a chore just to get the boys to understand they were going to pray together, and to get them lined up and sitting on the ground in some form of order. Now, they scrambled to their places in the line at the first streak of red sky, ready to end their day with a word to the Heavenly Father.

Josiah knew there were other things that needed his attention more urgently, but he felt compelled to drop his chores and write a letter home. He considered sending it to his parents, but then decided to send it for publication to the church periodical. *So that many more will pray*, he muttered to himself.

"October 23, 1907," he dated the page. "Greetings in the name of Our Precious Savior. Our silence of late has been largely due to much sickness with fever, cholera, etc. and the physical weakness that followed. We have been very near "the Border Land" at times, but the Father has seen fit to spare us yet for a while to the world so that we may labor for Him and for precious souls.

"When it seemed such a little way across into the glory world, I felt that for me it would be 'far better' to depart and be with Jesus, but there is still a desire to recover and live for the sake of others who need our help."

Josiah poured out several stories of little children from their orphanage who had come to know Christ before their illnesses and, praise be, passed to glory with the assurance of living in eternity.

"Please pray; the need is urgent," he wrote in closing. "Pray that we would have strength to share the soulsaving news of Christ with more children, and that their small hearts would accept it, before it's too late. Pray for their health, and for ours, which at times we feel hangs in the balance but by a slender thread. Yours in the fight for souls until the Lord calls us to our eternal home, Josiah Martin."

Could Josiah have imagined how soon that would be?

CHAPTER 5
THE NEXT WAVE

The Year 1908

"Mary, it's late," Noah said gently, taking his wife's hand–and the letter she still clutched in it. The letter, in the handwriting that Mary did not recognize, was from the mission in India, telling them of Rhoda's death from smallpox.

Their precious Rhoda had died just eighteen days after her beloved Josiah. It seemed impossible to believe.

Noah glimpsed the tear-stained face of his lovely wife and saw, with surprise, that deep wrinkles had settled into the creases by her eyes. How odd, he thought. He had never seen his beautiful wife look so old. "It's time for bed," he said aloud. "All this will still be here tomorrow. You need to rest. Rhoda would want that."

Mary could not shake herself away from the memories, even the bad ones. Seven years had passed since the death of Sara, Martha and Eber, yet the grief still seemed as raw and new as yesterday. And now Rhoda.

Noah looked upon his wife with a flood of sympathy. Could he have been wrong, wrong to plant so strong a seed of evangelism in his children? If he had not, they might still be here! The thought entered his head in a split second, and he knew at once it was from the Devil.

His wife, his partner in this rocky life where death had once again come knocking, met his eyes with hers, looking for some reassurance. They were God-fearing people who believed with all their soul and strength that nothing in this life was more important than telling others about the Savior and the assurance of eternal life. They had taught that and modeled that for their children, and they had excitedly and prayerfully watched four of them sail across the ocean to foreign lands to carry out the lessons well learned from their parents. That three of them had lost their lives doing this was inexplicable, and yet, had not the Lord sacrificed Himself for them as well? Noah knew this truth: That nothing happened to his children that had not first passed through the hand of God. He had allowed this; they must not question. They must have faith.

"Mary, my Mary," Noah said, taking her in his arms. "Rhoda is the happy one. She is with the Lord she loved so much. She died doing His work, His will. We must cling to that, Mary."

Mary nodded, but the grief that overtook her threatened to bring her to her knees. Then suddenly, she thought, what better place to be? She knelt then, right in the kitchen, by the well-worn, oak farm table, and placed her elbows on the oak bench. This bench, hewn by Noah's own hand when they were first married; this bench where each of her eight children had taken their meals everyday, where many an evening had passed pleasantly as they chattered away about the events of their days and their dreams for the future; this bench now offered her support as she raised her hands to the Lord in prayer. Noah knelt by her and enclosed her small hand with his.

"Dear God, we know not why you have taken Rhoda," she said softly. "Or our other children—Sara and Eber and Martha—who were trying to do Your will even as they departed this life." She paused to wipe a tear. "We grieve, dear Lord, and we beg of you, give us strength, give us courage, and most of all, dear Lord, guard our faith that we might not waver in what we know is true—that you love with a wonderful love and you will walk with us through all of life's trials. Let us feel you close, dear Lord. Be as close to us as you are to my precious babies, Rhoda, Sara, Martha, and Eber. I give them back to you, Lord, and in return, I ask your strength be upon me. Amen."

When Mary opened her eyes, a welcome peace flooded her soul. It was there, praise be, that peace that passes understanding. There would be more tears, more grief, more longing for what was now past, but her faith would undergird her and sustain her. Of that she felt sure. Just then, she saw it from the corner of one eye. She smiled. She remembered when she found these words, carved innocently in the bench by one first learning to spell her name. At the time, they had brought forth Mary's temper; now they brought her a smile. She ran her wrinkled hand over the letters, smiled and reread the words written more than twenty years ago "I love you" and "Rhoda."

Seeing the sweet smile on his wife's face, Noah relaxed too. "And she still does love you, Mary," he whispered.

As darkness crept over the kitchen, Noah lit a gas lamp and Mary got their supper, though neither was too eager to eat. Molasses bread and leftover soup would suffice.

"I suppose I should carry the news to some of the Brethren," Noah said as he cleaned his bowl with a swab of bread.

"There's time enough for that tomorrow," Mary said. "Tonight let it just be us, alone with our memories."

"Fair enough, then," Noah agreed. He paused, then spoke in a small voice that began to rise with his conviction, "Mary, Rhoda's light still shines. It is in the faces of those little children she left behind, and in the hearts of those natives she touched with her love, and in the souls of those people who will see her again on the other shore because of what she did."

"You are right now, aren't you, dear?" Mary sighed. "Rhoda had such confidence. Bring me her letter from last week." The letter, the last they would receive from their daughter, had been penned on December 31, just after her husband's passing.

"My Dear Papa and Mama," Noah read aloud again. "Bless the Lord, oh my soul! And all that is within me, bless His holy name! Perhaps you wonder at my starting out thus. It is only because God gives me such victory at this time when the waters are deep and the furnace is hot. I suppose that sometime today you will receive the word of dear Josiah's home going. Yes, our precious Josiah, your dear boy and my darling husband. Oh, is it true? Can it be? It is the same old story. He came in contact with smallpox somewhere. It has been at Raghunathpur and it goes through the air, you know."

"And to think, she had it too, even as she wrote this letter!" Mary interrupted.

"On Christmas a rash began to come out on him. On Friday, we noticed a blister on his chest, so we feared smallpox was developing," Noah continued.

"Skip over that next part," Mary instructed. She did not want to hear again the details of her son-in-law's gruesome overtaking by the pox.

"Tuesday morning before Christmas, I found Josiah weeping," Noah said, picking up in the middle of Rhoda's letter. "I said, 'Why are you weeping, dear?' He said, 'I was just thinking of what the Lord has done for me.' Another morning, I said, "Josiah, have you the victory?' He answered 'O yes,' with assurance. I said at another time, 'Josiah, we don't know but the Lord might take you home to heaven.' He said so sweetly, 'That would be precious.' All through this sickness and in spite of the cruel disease and his awful sufferings, he praised the Lord. Over and over, he would say, 'Precious Jesus, I am Thine and Thou art mine."

"On Saturday at about noon, he became perfectly rational and called for me. Brother Horst was with him and told him they are under quarantine. He said, 'Tell Rhoda good bye for me. I'm surely going this time. I am glad I came to India because I loved Jesus. Tell Rhoda to be

faithful. I'll see her again. Kiss the babies for me.
Tell all the missionaries to be faithful. It pays! It
pays! This is my desire: going to meet the Lord
from the jungles of India. It pays! It pays! I'd do it
again!" and he got so blessed he laughed 'til he
shook and said, 'Hallelujah!'"

Noah had to stop and wipe away a tear of his
own at the thought of his precious daughter
bearing this pain alone. He cleared his throat and
continued, "Oh it means so much for me to be left,
but God is so near, so wonderfully upholding me.
Your little girl is now a widow. The blow has
come so heavily and so unexpected. It would
seem most cruel had not Father dealt it. It has
been done in love," his daughter's words read.

"In love?" Mary questioned her husband. He
was silent for a while.

"We do not always understand God's ways,
Mary, but we must accept," Noah said. "God has
not promised us we will evade life's cruelties, but
that He will walk with us through them. He has
done that for us, Mary. He will do it again."

Mary wondered at the strength of her
daughter, to lay cotton and coconut husks and a
sheet in the crude coffin fashioned from boxes
from a shipment of some sort. "I specially wanted
to do this myself because it was the last time I
would ever make my husband's bed," Rhoda had
written. Tears threatened again as Mary thought
of the last time she made Rhoda's bed.

"A noble warrior has fallen but with victory,"
Noah said, reading the last paragraph of Rhoda's
letter. "There is a gap. Who will say, 'Here I am,

send me.' Who will rush to the battle front to fill the place? My heart echoes with Josiah's. I am glad I came to India, though it has cost me much. These five years have been full of toil and joy mingled with tears of sorrow. We have won the love of many of these brown faces. Blessed be the name of the Lord. Amen and amen. Lovingly, your child Rhoda."

Chapter Six
From Their Genes to Ours?

The Year 1909 and Years Following

As the years passed, Noah and Mary grew too old to carry on their evangelistic campaigns. At the invitation of their oldest daughter, Anna Zook George and her husband, Jacob, they moved to Goodman, Missouri in 1909, the year after Rhoda and Josiah died. They still found the strength to travel back home once in a while. One such trip occurred in the fall of 1911 when Noah and Mary came home to Kansas to participate in the Love Feasts.

"We never know but this may be our last trip home," Noah, now seventy, said to Mary as they entered the Abilene BIC Church. Noah was preparing to preach. Mary took his hand and squeezed it. "We have lived a rich life, you and I, Noah. We have not always understood God's ways, but we have accepted them. If it is to be our last trip, we will accept that too."

Noah preached that evening from I Thessalonians 5:24, "Faithful is he that calleth you, who also will do it."

Noah had been right; the next time he was present in that Abilene church, it was in body only. His spirit had passed to the "other shore" on February 6, 1912, where Mary was sure he was

once again embracing Eber, Sara, Martha, Rhoda
and Josiah. Noah's death was a blow to Mary. Her
partner in life, through its joyful and sorrowful ebb
and flow, was gone. The grief of losing a husband
she found quite different from that of losing her
children. It was a happier grief, somehow, if such a
thing is possible. She did not feel cheated by his
death; they had lived a long, happy life together.

The house seemed too still as Mary entered
the kitchen. Only the sound of the clock ticked
from the overhead cabinet. When did it get so
loud, Mary wondered.

She set down her bonnet on the long kitchen
table and, carrying her small travel bag in her other
hand, took tentative steps toward the bedroom she
and Noah shared at their daughter's home.

She opened the door slowly and cast her eyes
around the cozy room, resting her gaze on the
quilt-topped bed, freshly made and now devoid of
any extra sheets or medicines that might remind
her of Noah's last hours there. Without warning,
Mary burst into tears, keenly feeling the absence
of her nearest and dearest earthly friend.

"Oh Mother," Anna said, coming alongside
her and enveloping her in a hug. "We all shall
miss Father so. But you will be happy here again;
you'll see."

Mary sniffled and sighed, "I know, daughter, I
will be. I am so thankful for the good home I have,
but I cannot help but feel my loss, though my loss

is Noah's eternal gain." She paused, "And it will not be long until we shall meet again."

The long winter days were hard on Mary's spirit. When it grew dark in late afternoon, Mary would often light a candle in her bedroom and sit upon the chair where Noah had sat for many hours when he was feeling poorly in the two months before the Lord called him home. She would run her hand over the seat back, as if massaging Noah's back as she had so often done to offer comfort. And she would talk softly to her dear husband, hoping he could hear from heaven.

"Dear Noah, how I miss you!" she whispered. "We always bore all our grieving together. Each time the Lord called one of our children home, I looked to you and you always comforted me. Now you cannot do it. I must find comfort in the Lord alone; and He is ever present."

Mary reflected on all the lives that had been touched by her husband's preaching, by his urgings to put service to Christ before all else. So many young people had written to her after his death to tell her of the impact of his sermons on their lives. And, indeed, when she looked at her own children's lives, her husband's unmistakable plea to follow the Master at all costs was clearly imprinted upon them.

Mary again read her son David's tribute to his father, which he had sent to the church periodical. "Our first remembrance of him is of a man of a godly and prayerful life," David wrote from India, where he lamented that his father's weekly letters had ceased to come. David wrote of his father's faithfulness in preaching the doctrine of holiness as a definite work of grace, even to those who did not at first accept this way of thinking.

"And we must not forget his interest in foreign missions," David added. "His interest proved to be very practical indeed in laying his children so freely upon the altar of God for this work. He had little of this world's goods, but he gave his children and saw four of them sail at different times from the wharf at New York, three for India and one for South Africa. He felt it much when the news would come of one and another falling on the field." David recalled his last parting with his father three years prior: "Go my son, and God be with you," Noah had said. Noah never doubted that God would go with his children and watch over them, even unto death.

What was it, Mary wondered, that caused her husband to so freely offer up his children instead of clutching them to his breast and keeping them close by? Why, it was the certain knowledge that nothing in this life, including this life itself, was more important than bringing the soul-saving news of Christ to those who had never heard it! Mary smiled at that. She too believed this. The work of the cross coursed through their veins and gave them life just as much as the air they breathed!

Mary continued to live with her family in Missouri until the Lord called her home on July 27, 1926 at the age of eighty. She was buried next to her husband in the cemetery at Zion BIC.

Upon her death, her son Jacob Zook penned a tribute. It read in part, "Mother-the staunch refuge and the haven from childish fears and pain, you labored unceasingly with but one great thought: that we, your flesh and blood, should fulfill your lofty ideals and hopes. And always that unceasing smile of joy and eternal confidence begotten in your everlasting faith in God."

It was, no doubt, that confidence that gave Mary the strength she needed to offer so many of her precious children to God for His service, and to bear the pain of losing them when He took them home prematurely. "Not my will, but Thine," she would often say, and she meant it.

Epilogue

The missions efforts of the Zook family became somewhat legendary among the Kansas Brethren, who never forgot the holiness teachings of Noah Zook, the revival fires lit by David Zook and the sacrificial efforts made by the Zook children who felt called to serve in missions.

David Zook, the only Zook child to live a long life on the mission field, served forty years in India. Much of his time there centered on orphanage work for destitute children and widows in Calcutta. In this city nicknamed "city of the dead" for all its dreaded plagues and disease, David lost one of his own children to death. For Noah and Mary, this grandchild was another sacrifice made on behalf of their family's unwavering attempts at evangelism. Perhaps indicative of his selfless devotion to God, David wrote, "We feel no inclination to complain, but one can say from the heart, 'The Lord has taken away, blessed be the name of the Lord.'" David died in 1941 at the age of sixty-nine. Upon his death, his daughter wrote, "I wouldn't be a bit surprised if my father was responsible in a great measure for the beginning of missionary work in the Brethren in Christ Church."

When we look back on the lives of Noah and Mary Zook, their children, and Jesse Engle, what do we see? There are plenty of questions: How could a mother bear so graciously the loss of so many children on the mission field, where surely God should have been watching over them as they did His work? How could this same faith propel an aging man like Jesse Engle to forsake the comforts of home to embark on life in a remote African village, all because he wanted to tell the natives about Jesus? How could Josiah Martin, on his death bed, proclaim about his cross-cultural service, "It pays! It pays" when it cost him his own life? How could Rhoda Martin, just days after her husband's death, write so confidently that she knew her loving Father had dealt the death blow and so it was not cruel?

These early Brethren in Christ missionaries had one overwhelming thing in common: They were willing to risk everything for the sake of the Cross. And they truly counted it all—sacrifices and tragedies included—as their gain. What Jesse Engle, Francis Davidson, Sara Zook Cress and others began in Africa was not in vain. From their pioneering efforts have sprung schools, clinics, hospitals and church plants. Today, more than 100 years later, the Brethren in Christ Church in Zimbabwe boasts the largest national BIC membership worldwide.

Today, though our missionaries do not normally face smallpox or many of the other life-threatening conditions that plagued early missionaries, they share in many of the challenges that have been part of a cross-cultural calling since the Apostle Paul's first forays among people of other cultures. Often misunderstood by those they serve, forgotten by those who sent, separated from family and friends, stalked by loneliness, tempted by the seductive lure of comfort, and, yes, at times still, placing themselves in settings of physical risk—they press on in response to the love of Christ that constrains them. Responding with joy to the privilege of walking 'on mission with God'–engaged in God's Kingdom–building work, winning souls for eternity, just as the Zook children did before them.

So we are left with the final question: What is in our spiritual DNA that began in the lives of people like Jesse Engle and David Zook? The Brethren in Christ place a high value on servanthood and evangelism. How will that play out across the history pages of this denomination yet to be written?

In the words of Brethren in Christ World Missions Executive Director John Brubaker, "The same God that called David Zook and Jesse Engle calls us to step out in faith to see the Kingdom of God established . . . We're asking God to raise up a new generation that is willing to live life on the edge, willing to take great risks so that His mission and His love will be multiplied across the earth."

These chapters are based on the true story of the Noah and Mary Zook family. They contain information from the Brethren in Christ Archives and include fictional embellishments by the author, Carolyn Kimmel. Factual information and some quotes from Clifford Cress are taken from his copyrighted autobiography and are used with permission from his grandson H. Franklin Bloomer Jr., and Kent Bloomer, Riverside, CT.

LIVING THE BRETHREN IN CHRIST MANDATE

Dr. Paitoon looked around the group, eyes shining. Pastor of a large church in Bangkok, Thailand, he had worked with Brethren in Christ missionaries and knew their passion. He had seen their commitment and sensed their hunger to see the church grow in his land. Now he was speaking to furloughed and potential missionaries for all Brethren in Christ fields of service, along with various staff and board members, at the annual workshop in Pennsylvania.

Paitoon had chosen to speak from Ezekiel 47—the passage about a trickle of water escaping from under the threshold of the temple towards the east. As he described the vision, it was easy to picture how the man of God showed Ezekiel that water was also beginning to flow out on the south side. He had a measuring line and as he went from place to place, the water rose steadily. At first it was ankle deep. Then it rose to knee deep. A thousand cubits on it was up to the man's hips. Soon it was so deep that Ezekiel could not walk through—he must swim. It was now a river!

Together we followed the message as Dr. Paitoon developed the verses describing many trees by the river, the river turning fresh, and then the verdant life springing up wherever it flowed! On the banks now grew all kinds of trees for food. The fruit never failed, month by month, because the river flowed from the sanctuary. The leaves never withered, but instead provided healing for all.

Practical applications followed, and each of us could see the glorious Gospel of Christ bringing life to the nations. We could see the Brethren in Christ doing our share to swell the river. Tears welled up as we saw our own individual parts in submitting to the flow and going where and how the Lord carried us to bless the nations.

It was a sacred moment as we sat at the feet of our brother, won to Christ as an international student on an American campus, now reaching out to his own people in an unevangelized land and tutoring the missionaries who came to help. Later, Dr. Paitoon and his wife ministered in the evening service by laying their hands on any who needed a fresh anointing of the Holy Spirit, and praying for them. It became clear that although we had not been the ones to lead the Paitoons to Christ, the sending of our missionaries was bringing great blessing to the denomination.

Personal benefit is not one of the reasons we generally think of for sending missionaries, but there are lists of blessings that come to those who share Christ cross-culturally. There are blessings to the goers and blessings to the senders—and it is not wrong to count these blessings. There are many other reasons, however, for going and sending. When we think of the thousands of groups of people that still do not have ways of hearing the Gospel, we are sobered. They need to hear! The need is enormous! We need to go!

When we experience mercy, forgiveness, and wholeness in our lives, we have a tremendous longing to share God's grace with those who have not heard about it. Then there is God's heart for all the nations as He speaks of them throughout Scripture, and His clear call and command to go and preach and teach them. Finally, there is a specific mandate that God lays on the hearts of certain individuals and groups of people whom He has blessed with His presence and guidance.

Do we Brethren in Christ hold in our hands a specific mandate from God that we need to fulfill? And if we do, what is it? Where did we get it? And how do we carry it out?

We like to look at our Anabaptist background and ponder the influences that formed us. We may be unaware of the fact that from January 21, 1525 when the believers' church broke with state church leader Zwingli over the issue of baptism, the re-baptizers' program was evangelism. According to Glenny and Smallman in *Missions in a New Millenium*, no text was referred to more often by the Anabaptists than Matthew 28, and the believers were tortured, drowned, and burned by the thousands because they would not stop preaching!

They worshipped wherever they could, baptizing believers and taking communion together. Their main method of evangelizing was through house churches—those functioning bodies of believers engaging in Bible study, discussion, question and answer periods, and prayer sessions. In the meetings they stressed that people are free to choose and that we make decisions for or against Christ—we do not automatically become Christians by being baptized as infants. The small meetings grew to be large assemblies of people. In only a few months, a Bible study in the home of a man named John Kessler expanded into a hall to seat 1000!

In the early stages the Anabaptists also used open-air evangelism —street meetings were not an invention of the 1900s. Bolt Eberli was a peasant preacher who spoke forth for a few weeks in the spring of 1525. He was burned at the stake and became the first martyr of the Swiss brethren. But others took his place. Other methods of evangelism included invitations to public meetings and door-to-door witnessing. Townspeople complained that at times hundreds of Anabaptists would go out to preach. Several times there were demonstrations.

When public debates were held, the educated churchmen thought it would be easy for them to trounce their opponents, but the simple, keen wit and extensive Bible knowledge of the Anabaptists carried the day. There were also "commercial missionaries." Esther Carpentier, seller of sewing notions, evangelized whole towns. There were peddlers, wandering journeymen and artisans who carried their message with their wares.

But of all the methods of evangelism, cross-bearing and martyrdom seemed to be the most effective in winning converts. Suffering, and the opportunity to witness that came with it, were considered normal for the believers. They felt themselves to be in spiritual union with Christ in his suffering, and a theology of suffering was taught in nearly all Anabaptist writings. Often the people looking on were moved to sympathize, and sometimes the tormentors were converted. The Anabaptists were known for the soundness and authenticity of their spiritual lives—and they refused to fight back!

Some feared that this principle would, perhaps, be their undoing. How could they keep evangelizing others if they were continually mown down? Michael Sattler, an ex-monk became convinced that it was even wrong to slay the invading Muslim Turks. Such madness, and the radical pacifism that developed, emerged as Sattler and the believers met secretly to draw up their simple theology. They were discovered. Sattler was imprisoned and burned at the stake, as were thousands of others in the days that followed, but the theology of peace lives on and enlightens our Brethren in Christ mandate today.

Persecution took its toll. Many Anabaptists fled to Holland and on to the United States. Others stayed. Gradually the feeling grew that a silent witness could be effective. They would pursue a simple lifestyle with honest dealings and good relations with neighbors and draw people to God in this way. But many became ingrown, and historians say that they became incapable of outside evangelism. It took the revival movement of Pietism to bring back an evangelistic spirit to some Anabaptist churches.

And Pietism is also a part of our heritage. The emphasis on a changed heart, obedience to God's word, and righteous living created a hunger and a moving towards God that was contagious. A third component, Wesleyanism, brought with it an emphasis on true discipleship and the power of the Holy Spirit. It is significant that Wesleyanism took root among the Brethren in Christ in Kansas, the same part of the church where the Brethren in Christ missions movement began.

These three streams of spiritual development have formed our unique theological and practical DNA. We must ask ourselves to what degree we as Brethren in Christ have a special mandate to share our understanding and love for God with the world.

At an Ignite meeting for those discerning God's call to long-term missions the speaker was Ruth Veltkamp, a missionary used by God to start a movement among Muslim leaders in northern Nigeria. Ruth explained that when one of these leaders puts his faith in Christ, he is immediately persecuted by other Muslims. He may be beaten, imprisoned, cursed or poisoned. His house may be destroyed and his wife and family taken from him.

Some believers die from the ill treatment. Others survive and give testimonies to the tremendous power that Christ gives them to forgive. The persecutors are amazed at God's provision and a whole circle of them may turn to Christ as a result. Gradually the Muslim background believers have developed a theology of forgiveness that releases, restores, blesses—and especially evangelizes.

When Ruth heard of the Brethren in Christ longing and preparation for a focus on outreach to

Muslims, she was encouraged. Then she heard of our peace position and was impressed even further. "You are already there on the theology of forgiveness," she said. "This will be a powerful weapon with which to meet whatever Muslim peoples God leads you to approach."

And we do have a track record. In some parts of our international community, we already know much about persecution. Our Indian brothers and sisters have seen commitment unto death by the first Brethren in Christ martyr of the century. His widow still lives among them. In every part of the international church we know something of suffering—among both the missionaries and the national converts. The question is: Are our missionaries willing to pay the price? And are we willing to give our brightest and best to such a cause?

The cost is high. A few of the number who gave their lives on the field are founding father Jesse Engle; superintendent Henry Steigerwalt, whose personal nurse stayed on to serve into her seventies and still lives at Messiah Village; Amos Ginder (great uncle of a mission board member) who died of typhoid fever at Matopo Mission after only a few years of service; and Marie Traver who died of cerebral malaria after only a few months of service in Zambia.

Others of us have needed courage to serve in the midst of political turmoil. We have had political activists with burning branches dance around our sleeping hut with its dry grass roof, and have gotten rid of our hunting guns so as not to be tempted to protect the family through violence. Others have suffered devastating motor accidents or chronic fatigue syndrome. Still others have persevered after paralyzing bicycle accidents. Even having our children grow up without the presence of grandparents, or saying goodbye to the prospects of marriage have become major sacrifices for some of us.

Yes, the cost is high. We need to be sure of our mandate, our calling and our motives. Dr. Paitoon's message about the river came from Ezekiel 47:1-10. We took it personally, but the context shows that it is for the world. Isaiah and Zechariah saw Ezekiel's vision of temple, throne, and river as God's universal invitation to the nations—a global missionary program. Jesus later directed the vision to himself with the woman at the well. It is clear that we dare never keep the life-giving flow of God's truth to ourselves.

We have a mandate. However small the Brethren in Christ, we have precious truth and experience to share. Are we willing to live the mandate we have been given? Do we have the courage to live it to the full and die for it as well? This is what Brethren in Christ World Missions is about. The challenge will be to both carry out our mandate, and partner with others as well—to be loyal to our heritage and at the same time to be innovative and creative—to be faithful to our legacy and to catch fresh fire. God alone will enable us to fulfill the mandate he has given.

Grace Holland (Chair, Board for World Missions, 1999-2006)

The preceeding pages chronicle the rebirth of this mandate on a global scale for the Brethren in Christ—as seen through the eyes of those most intimately involved in its inception. As you re-live these events that unfolded over a century ago, we pray that you will carry away a clear sense of the compelling vision that grew from a passionate pursuit of God – a passion that eventually enabled this group to touch the world with a message of hope. A subsequent volume chronicles the individual stories that resulted in outreach beyond those first few points of global ministry. We anticipate that you will be challenged by stories of those who have gone before us—giving us a godly heritage that is expressed today in different forms but that continues to be fueled by that same passionate pursuit of God.

John Brubaker (Executive Director Brethren in Christ World Missions, 1999-2008)

Sources

For more on the lives of Noah and Mary Zook, read *The History of the Brethren in Christ Church* by A.W. Climenhaga. For more on Mary Zook's spiritual conversion, read "A Sister's Religious Experience" in *The Evangelical Visitor*, May 1, 1888. To read about the evangelism efforts of the Zooks, look up their names in the index files of The *Evangelical Visitor* to find many articles.

For more on the life of David Zook, read "D.W. Zook: The Life of the First Brethren in Christ Missionary to India" by Elwood A. Pye, in "Notes and Queries in Brethren in Christ History" July 1968. There are also many of David Zook's writings in the pages of the *Evangelical Visitor*, catalogued in the archives.

For more on the life of Clifford Cress and his wife, Sara Zook Cress, read his autobiography in his own hand, titled "Among the Matabele" in the BIC Archives. There you will learn an interesting twist to his life story—he later met up with and married Amanda Zook, the widow of his brother-in-law Eber Zook.

For more on Eber Zook's death, read Amanda Zook's letters, stored in the BIC Archives, and read David Zook's memoir of his brother in the *Evangelical Visitor*, February 15, 1901.

For more on Rhoda and Josiah Martin's deaths, read "A Missionary's Letter to her Parents" in the archives.

For those who may wonder what became of Esther and Everett Martin, the twin orphans of Rhoda and Josiah Martin–they were brought from India to Pennsylvania by their uncle, David Zook. From there, they were taken to Missouri and raised by Rhoda's sister, Anna Catherine Zook George and her husband, Jacob George, until their teen years. Everett moved back to Lancaster County, where he married and became a farmer. Esther married a man whom she met on the carousel at the World's Fair in Chicago and eventually lived in California. The twins did not remain close to each other. They rarely spoke of the parents they never knew or of their sacrifice for missions. Everett's son, Richard Martin, who lives in Manheim, Pennsylvania has done research on the Martin family. "Almost everything I know about my father's family, I know from my own research," Richard says. "I'm quite proud of what that family gave for the cause of missions. They were an unusual family."

For more on Jesse Engle, read his personal file in the archives, complete with letters in his own handwriting to his children. There is also a typewritten file of his letters, compiled and edited by Adam Tarantino. Two books that contain information on Jesse Engle are *There is No Difference* by Anna Engle, J.A. Climenhaga and Leoda A. Buckwalter, and *The History of the Brethren in Christ Church* by Climenhaga.

For more on Frances Davidson's missionary efforts, read her book, *South and South Central Africa*. She is also featured in the book *Nine Portraits* by E. Morris Sider.

For more on Rhoda Lee, read *Searching for Rhoda Lee* by Helen Johns.

TIMELINE

1888–Noah and Mary Zook are named traveling missionaries of the River Brethren (later renamed Brethren in Christ)

1894–David Zook holds evangelistic meetings in his Kansas home congregation of Zion that stir hearts toward foreign missions

1894–Rhoda Lee gives a bold speech on the floor of general conference, calling the brethren to commence foreign mission work

1896–David Zook and his wife Katie go out as faith missionaries to Japan

1897–Frances Davidson, Jesse and Elizabeth Engle, Barbara Hershey and Alice Heise become the first Brethren in Christ Missionaries, in Africa

1898–David and Katie Zook leave Japan to begin work in India; Eber and Amanda Zook embark on a missions effort to India later that year

1899–Sara Zook Cress and her husband, Clifford Cress, sail for Africa, to join Jesse Engle and his team

1900–Sara Zook Cress dies in Africa from malarial fever; Eber dies from smallpox late that same year; Jesse Engle also passes away in Africa, from malaria

1903–Rhoda Zook Martin and her husband, Josiah, depart for mission work in India

1906–Frances Davidson, with Adda Engle, sets out to establish Macha mission in Zambia

1907–Josiah Martin dies of smallpox on December 30

1908–Rhoda Zook Martin dies from the same disease 18 days later. Two other missionaries, Amos G. Horst and Thaddeus Vaughan also died from smallpox in the same month. At the direction of the civil service physician, the mission building was burned.

1912–Noah Zook passes away

1923–Frances Davidson returns home from Africa

1926–Mary Zook passes away

1934–David Zook returns home, having finished his missions efforts in India

1935–Frances Davidson passes away

1941–David Zook passes away in Tabor, Iowa

THE MISSIONARIES' HOME-GOING

There are tragedies in human life far more real than those exhibited in an opera. There are heroes and heroines whose names are not recorded in history and whose names never will be recorded, compared to whom Dewey, Hobson and Roosevelt would sink into oblivion or pale as does the moon before the rising sun. Among such are the lives which form the subject of this song. We have known of one family furnishing several boys as targets for the foe and we honor the mother who gladly gives her boy as a sacrifice for the country's need. But there is another battle a great invisible conflict which requires men, and women too, of more courage than is required to go out and face the rain of shot and shell on the battle field. And happy is the father and mother who furnishes one child for this great battle against sin and the devil; but who can tell of the blessedness of the parent who gives not one, but two; not two but several? Such a father and mother are Mr. and Mrs. Noah Zook, formerly of Dickinson Co., Kans., now living in Goodman, Mo., U.S.A. The first to lead the way across the dark sea as a Missionary to India was their son, David Zook⋯

The second chorus of this song refers to the ZOOK children of whom only one remains of the four who left for the foreign shore. It should be sung after the last stanza.

Yours in Jesus' name

HERBERT BUFFUM, Evangelist

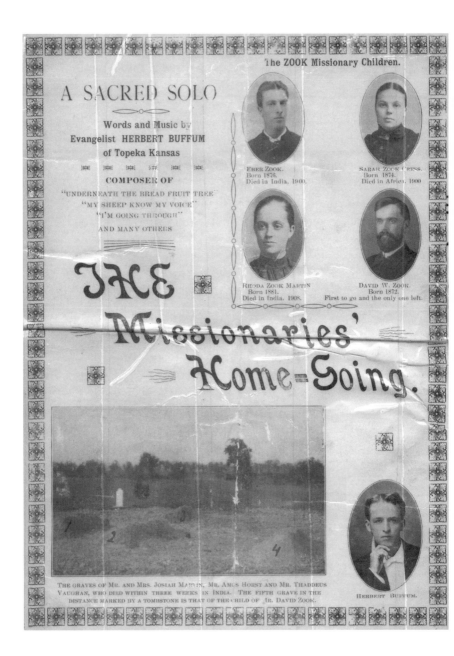

The ZOOK Missionary Children.

A SACRED SOLO

Words and Music by
Evangelist HERBERT BUFFUM
of Topeka Kansas

COMPOSER OF

"UNDERNEATH THE BREAD FRUIT TREE"
"MY SHEEP KNOW MY VOICE"
"I'M GOING THROUGH"
AND MANY OTHERS

THE
Missionaries'
Home-Going.

EBER ZOOK.
Born 1876.
Died in India, 1900.

SARAH ZOOK CRESS.
Born 1874.
Died in Africa, 1900.

RHODA ZOOK MARTIN
Born 1881.
Died in India, 1908.

DAVID W. ZOOK.
Born 1872.
First to go and the only one left.

THE GRAVES OF MR. AND MRS. JOSIAH MARTIN, MR. AMOS HORST AND MR. THADDEUS
VAUGHAN, WHO DIED WITHIN THREE WEEKS IN INDIA. THE FIFTH GRAVE IN THE
DISTANCE MARKED BY A TOMBSTONE IS THAT OF THE CHILD OF MR. DAVID ZOOK.

HERBERT BUFFUM.

THE MISSIONARIES' HOME-GOING.

There are tragedies in human life far more real than those exhibited in an opera. There are heroes and heroines whose names are not recorded in history and whose names never will be recorded, compared to whom Dewey, Hobson and Roosevelt would sink into oblivion or pale as does the moon before the rising sun. Among such are the lives which form the subject of this song. We have known of one family furnishing several boys as targets for the foe and we honor the mother who gladly gives her boy as a sacrifice for the country's need. But there is another battle a great invisible conflict which requires men, and women too, of more courage than is required to go out and face the rain of shot and shell on the battle field. And happy is the father and mother who furnishes one child for this great battle against sin and the devil: but who can tell of the blessedness of the parent who gives not one, but two; not two but several? Such a father and mother are Mr. and Mrs. Noah Zook, formerly of Dickinson Co., Kans., now living in Goodman, Mo., U. S. A. The first to lead the way across the dark sea as a Missionary to India was their son

DAVID W. ZOOK

who, after spending two years in Japan arrived in India in Febuary 1898. The second to leave for India was another son

EBER ZOOK

who, arrived in December 1898. He toiled faithfully for his Lord in that darkened land in Calcutta) just a few days over a year died of Confluent Small Pox, December 1900. His last words were. "IT WOULD BE ALL GLORY!" One cannot be a student of human nature in any degree without reading in his innocent, noble face the inward purity of his soul. The third to leave for the heathen land was

SARA ZOOK CRESS

who with her husband, Clifford Cress, reached South Africa sometime in 1898, was called to meet her Lord even before her brother Eber, as she passed away Feb. 8th, 1900. No sweeter character ever walked this sinful earth. Every one who sees her picture speaks of "that remarkable face." We have quite an extended account of this young missionary's life published in connection with the song. '*Underneath the Bread-fruit Tree*.' As she was passing away a beautiful smile hovered on her countenance, and as the friends bent over her bedside, they heard her say, "THE VEIL IS TAKEN AWAY."
The next to sail for dark India, was.

RHODA ZOOK MARTIN

and her husband Josiah Martin. It was their privilege to toil almost five years in India for God. But there came a time when quite a number of the missionaries had met for "communion sweet", and death came also. It was discovered in a short time that Josiah Martin had the same disease of which his wife's brother, Eber, had died. After he had been ill for some time his wife said to him: "Josiah, we

don't know but that the Lord may take you home to heaven." He said, "That would be precious." Over and over he would say, "Precious Jesus, I am Thine and Thou art mine." 'Sometimes just after a vomit of blood, he would say, 'Hallelujah!' 'Not a shadow could rise, not a cloud dim the skies.' Later he said, 'I'm glad I came to India because I love Jesus. TELL RHODA TO BE FAITHFUL.' I'll see her again! Kiss the babies for me! Tell all the missionaries to be faithful! IT PAYS! IT PAYS!!'" Later he said to his wife, "'Tell father to take courage; His way is so changed from ours This is my desire. GOING TO MEET MY LORD FROM THE JUNGLES OF INDIA! IT PAYS IT PAYS!' and he got so blest he laughed till he shook, and said, 'HALLELUJAH!' OH, I PRAYED IT MIGHT STIR THE HEARTS OF THOSE ASLEEP AT HOME!" These facts are taken from a letter written by his wife shortly after the death of her husband, and only a few days before her sickness and translation. On January 17th the third of the ZOOK children

RHODA

went to meet her husband from whom she had been separated so shortly. Her last conscious words, spoken with a heavenly smile on her scarred face (referring to the dying words of her husband) "JOSIAH SAID, 'I'LL SEE HER AGAIN.'" Through their translation twin babies were left, Ester and Eevertt. The same day Sister RHODA Z. MARTIN passed away, died another one, one who had compassion on those who were afflicted—Brother AMOS HORST, who had been there since October 1905. He left a widow and a small boy, Eber. His last words were, "IT IS WELL WITH MY SOUL, BUT MY GLORY WILL NOT BE FULL TILL I GET OVER YONDER." His wife had the same wonderful victory that characterized Sister Rhoda Martin after her husband had been taken. About four days latter January 21st the fourth one to be taken within three weeks was another who gave his life to nurse those who were afflicted Brother THADDEUS VAUGHAN. His last words were, "I HAVE LIVED A RIGHTEOUS LIFE!" He had spent about the same length of time in India as brother Horst and left a bride of three months. God sustained her in the same miraculous manner as the others. But the one who suffered the most, the hero who watched over the bedside of all; who made his own sister's coffin and buried her; the one who led the way from the old farm in Dickinson County, and watched one by one his loved ones join him in the foreign fields, and one by one laid them away—the one left out of "four who went away" to fight on till Jesus says "come up higher," is

DAVID

who with his noble self-sacrificing wife will still continue in the darkened land in defiance of disease, poverty, and the darkness of heathen prejudice,

* * * * * * * * * * * * *

The second chorus of this song refers to the ZOOK children of whom only one remains of the four who left for the foreign shore. It should be sung after the last stanza.
Yours in Jesus' name
HERBERT BUFFUM, Evangelist

A MISSIONARY'S LETTER
To Her Parents.

Sripat Purunia, Bankura Dist., Bengal, India.

Dec. 31, 1907.

My Dear Papa and Mamma:—

"Bless the Lord, Oh my soul! and all that is within me, Bless His holy name!" Perhaps you wonder at my starting out thus. It is only because God gives me such victory at this time when the waters are deep and the furnace is hot. 'I suppose that sometime to-day you will receive the word of dear Josiah's home going. Yes, our precious Josiah, your dear boy and my darling husband. Oh can it be? It is the same old story. He came in contact with the smallpox somewhere. It has been at Raghunathpur and it goes through the air you know. He hadn't felt well for a couple of weeks and yet we still took a trip up country, he going, on to Lucknow and having a visit with Brother Mussers'. He felt it so on his heart to visit them. He felt the Lord was leading him to go and they had such a nice time together and explained some things and they seemed to understand some things in a way they hadn't before. He felt blessed in having gone. I will tell you more later. I met him at Mugalsari and then we went to Benares together, were at Arrah Sunday and on Monday we came here. He went to bed as soon as we got here and felt very sick that night. Each succeeding day

2.

found him worse. On Christmas a rash began to come out on him and we called the native doctor from Malsaram who said it was probably a mild form of measles. Of course, it wasn't developed for him really to say. On Friday, we noticed a blister on his chest, so we feared small pox was developing. We wired for the civil Surgeon at Bankura, 20 miles away. The wire was sent at 9:30 A. M. and he was here about 1:30 P. M. having come up on his motor bicycle. He pronounced it confluent small pox the very kind Eber had. He left a prescription for some stuff to wash his throat to and swab it and some to drop in his eyes, but said they don't give much medicine in small pox. From Monday night, he vomited so much. At first it was bile, then black slimy stuff and then blood, though some blackish in appearance. His throat was so bad on Saturday, we feared he would choke but that was a little better and yesterday morning he passed away at 1 o'clock without a struggle. Brother Horst was with him and he noticed he acted like he was breathing his last. He came over to call David, went back and Josiah gave one more gasp and was gone. Gone to be with Jesus whom he loved so well, who was his "all in all. It seemed my spirit went with him to heaven's gates and I could not help thinking of the wonderful welcoming time they were having there.

We did'nt rebel when Father took his mother last October, but we thought if she could have been spared

3.

a little longer, then we would have seen her once more. Josiah took it so well though, of course he shed some tears and wrote father such a touching letter. He spoke of seeing her smiling face last on the platform at the Elizabethtown depot and said she will not be there to welcome us when we return. How little he thought that so soon she would meet him on heaven's threshold, to welcome him to his eternal home. What a strange, sweet Providence!

From the time that Josiah took sick last Monday (yesterday a week ago, rather) there was something peculiar about it. On our way out from Rauigaura here when he was feeling so badly, he repeated that hymn all through, "If ever I loved Thee, My Jesus 'Tis Now," and I thought at that time, this may mean something, and from that time, I felt so strangely about his sickness.

Jan 1, 1908

I will now resume my writing; I felt so tired yesterday I thought I would finish it later so now I will take up just where I left off.

Tuesday morning before Christmas. I found Josiah weeping. I said, "Why are you weeping dear?" He said, "I was just thinking of what the Lord has done for me." Another morning either Christmas or Thursday I said, "Josiah have you the victory?" He answered, "O yes" with assurance. I said at another time, "Josiah, we don't know but the Lord might take you home to heaven." He said so sweetly, "That would be precious.'

4.

All through this sickness in spite of the cruel disease and his awful sufferings, he praised the Lord. Over and over he would say "Precious Jesus, I am thine and thou art mine." and sometimes just after a vomit of blood he would say, "Hallelujah!" "Not a shadow rise not a cloud in the skies." It was sweeping victory for him all the way through. Oh I say such a home going! I know he had an abundant entrance into the pearly gates. He was delirious a good deal of the time but still he knew a great deal of what was going on. On Saturday at about noon, he became perfectly rational and called for me. Brother Horst was with him and told him they are under quarentine and he said, "Tell Rhoda good-bye for me. I'm surely going this time. I am glad I came to India because I loved Jesus. Tell Rhoda to be faithful. I'll see her again. Kiss the babies for me. Tell all the missionaries to be faithful. "It pays! It pays!" Again he called for me so I went in. I was in the next room and heard him say the foregoing. I asked him if he could see me. His dear eyes were nearly shut but he said he could see me and he saw some of the rest who were there. His eyes were so full of the pox but it didn't go over the pupil. I asked him if he had any message for Father Martin. He said, "Tell father to take courage. His way is so changed from ours. This is my desire: going to meet my Lord from the jungles of India. It pays! It pays! I,d do it again! I'd do it again!" and he got so blessed, he laughed till he shook, and

5.

said, "Hallelujah!" We all were blessed. Oh, I prayed it might stir the hearts of those who are asleep at home and that these words may burn their way into such as heated irons. Amen and Amen. Who says it doesn't pay? Oh, I'm glad for this dying testimony of dear Josiah. I asked him, "You have no regrets?" "No."

He wanted the rest who were here to come in and they had come before he said what he did for father, and they remained to hear the rest. When Brother Vaugham came in, he said, "Well Brother Martin, how is it?" He answered, "It's all glory. Hallelujah! Tell father and mother Zook they led me home.

"Dear little Esther and Everett, God bless them. God bless them. The Lord will give you wisdom, dear Rhoda, to train them for Him. Look up! Look up! I've tried to do what I could. I've tried to do my best." Then he wanted to be remembered very kindly to some of his special friends and a message for a native gentlemen at Raghunathpur in whose salvation he was so much interested. He also asked if we couldn't wait to bury him until the others could come from Raghunathpur. I spoke with him then and told him we had walked together for nearly eight years and that if I am to go on alone now I know the Lord will be with me and I wanted him to know I am willing for the Lord to have His way. We asked him if he wouldn't like to get well. He said, "The Will of the Lord be done." We didn't talk with him

6.

any longer. It was thought best that we leave the room, so I bade my precious Josiah a final farewell and I never saw him again. He looked so badly after that that I preferred to remember him as I told him "Farewell" and he answered "Yes."

Oh, it means so much for me to be left, but God is so near, so wonderfully upholding me. Your little girl is now a widow. The blow has come so heavily and so unexpected. It would seem most cruel had not the Father delt it. It has been done in love.

Dear Josiah has outstripped me in the race. His work was finished. His last mission was to Lucknow. God has said, "Come up higher." He has taken an eternal furlough from this sinful sorrowful world, hallelujah!

When we laid Josiah to rest here in the mission cemetery Monday evening at about 5:30 o'clock, God was with us. As I stood by his open grave, I could not help thanking God for his precious life, and He does not allow me to feel that dear Josiah is in the grave. When I think of the grave, the Spirit seems to point upward and say, "He's there."

During Josiah's sickness, he was thoughtful of me and one morning he noticed I was doing something (I was crocheting) and asked me what I am doing? I told him and then he said, "You must take care of yourself, dear." Once he asked if I don't rest in the day time. At another time when I was standing over his bed, he said with such meaning, "Courage!" It means so much to me now.

7.

The dear native boys were so faithful in helping. Two of them were in quarantine with the brethren who were caring for him and they never complained a word, that we know of, and worked so hard and washed out the bloody towels and things and they and four others of the boys carried him to the grave. Bros. Vaughan and Horst made the coffin. It was made of boxes that came out in some shipment or other. It was lined with white muslin and covered with black cloth and looked real nice. I helped some with it. I fixed some cotton and cocoanut husks in below for him to lie on and then I laid a sheet on top of that. I specially wanted to do this myself because it was the last time I would ever make his bed. I still feel it is the Lord's will for me to come home. I am looking to the Lord to make a way, and to raise up a traveling companion, who would be willing to help me with the children. I don't think I will get to sail before March 1st. I shall expect you dear ones to meet me at the wharf. You will won't you please?

God has wonderfully sustained me and is wonderfully doing so, but don't forget to pray for me. I know you won't. It seems wonderful that Josiah was the one that was taken when I was so low so long, and have been so frail so much of the time since. My heart has been standing the strain pretty well. I have had it examined and the doctors said there is no organized disease for which I am thankful.

The babies and Eber and Pauline are at Raghunathpur. We sent them up last week as it was thought safest. Sisters Horst and Vaughan took them up. Sister Horst is very fond of my little son and Sister Grace Vaughan of Esther so I know they will be well cared for. Dear baby Esther loved her Papa so.

8.

They were so attached to each other. The day she went to R— I think it was, I said "Mamma's Baby" and she said "Papa's, Papa's" I am so glad that they both learned to say papa but they'll not remember him as they grow up. I think I shall change Everett's name to Josiah Everett instead of Abram Everett. I am sending you a good picture of them. Hope to get it off this week.

We had a short service at Josiah's grave. Sang Jesus Lover of My Soul, and The Day When the Trumpet Sounds and Praise God From Whom all Blessings Flow. The 102 Psalm from 11 verse and Psalm 102 were read and had prayer, it was in Bengali. Memorial services will be held later There was much rejoicing mingled with tears, some praised the Lord with a loud voice.

A noble warrior has fallen but with victory. There is a gap. Who will say, "Here am I, send me." Who will rush to the battle front to fill the place? My heart echoes with Josiah's, I'm glad I came to India, though it has cost me much. These five years have been full of toil and joy mingled with tears of sorrow.

These last months dear Josiah has been more useful than ever. He made a typical missionary. He had won the love of many of these brown faces. Blessed be the name of the Lord. "Amen and Amen. Lovingly your child

RHODA.

Sister Martin and Brother Amos G. Horst both fell asleep on January 17th, and on the 21st of the same month, the fourth one of the mission band, Thaddeus Vaughan also went to his reward, all from the same dread disease, small pox.

PRICE—50 cents per 100; $4.00 per 1000. Send 20 cents for package of assorted tracts. L. F. SHEETZ, Florin, Pa.